C000224596

STUDENT DRAMA SERIES

General Editor: MICHAEL MARLAND, B.A.

JOBY

JOBY

A TELEVISION PLAY
BY STAN BARSTOW
DRAMATIZED FROM HIS OWN NOVEL

EDITED BY MARILYN DAVIES

BLACKIE *LONDON AND GLASGOW*

Blackie & Son Limited
BISHOPBRIGGS
GLASGOW G64 2NZ
450 EDGWARE ROAD
LONDON W2 1EG

Joby   © Stan Barstow, 1975
As a published work © Stan Barstow, 1977
Notes and questions © Blackie & Son Limited, 1977

FIRST PUBLISHED 1977
ISBN 0 216 90180 4

PRINTED IN GREAT BRITAIN BY
WESTERN PRINTING SERVICES LTD, BRISTOL

CONTENTS

ACKNOWLEDGMENTS

The editor is grateful to the following for their help in the preparation of this volume:

Harvey Unna and Stephen Durbridge Ltd, Authors' Agents, for permission to print two extracts from the novel, *Joby*, by Stan Barstow.
Yorkshire Television Limited for the photographs from the Yorkshire Television production of *Joby*.

Joby

by Stan Barstow

TO JAMES ORMEROD,
who brought it to life on the small screen

Joby was a Yorkshire Television colour production for the ITV Network, and was first transmitted in two episodes on 12 and 19 January, 1975.

The principal players were as follows:

Reg Weston	Patrick Stewart
Joby Weston	Richard Tolan
Norah Weston	Diana Davies
Snap	David Clayforth
Gus Wilson	Martin Whiteley
Aunt Daisy	Lorraine Peters
Cousin Mona	Sharon Gower
Molly MacLeod	Joanne Whalley

Produced and directed by James Ormerod.
Executive Producer, Peter Willes.

Joby *takes place in August, 1939, in a small Yorkshire township—a working town of textile mills and a coalmine, but with open fields and a river close at hand.*

THE CHARACTERS

JOBY WESTON
NORAH WESTON, his mother
REG WESTON, his father

AUNT DAISY, his mother's sister
UNCLE TED, Aunt Daisy's husband
COUSIN MONA, their daughter

SNAP
GUS WILSON
TOMMY MASTERMAN
AUDREY
AUDREY'S FRIEND
MOLLIE MACLEOD
AGNES, her sister

MR MORRISON, headmaster of Joby's primary school
MR LAEDECKER
MRS LAEDECKER
ELSA LAEDECKER
MAN WITH GREYHOUND
MR MANLEY, the barber
FIRST OLD MAN }
SECOND OLD MAN } at the barber's
CINEMA ATTENDANT
NURSING SISTER
PREACHER
CHEMIST
GROCER
MRS COLLINS, a neighbour

Other boys and girls, speaking and non-speaking: in the cinema, at play, in school, and others.
Other adults, speaking and non-speaking: soldier, ambulance man, chapel congregation and others.

ACTING NOTE

All rights in this play are strictly reserved. Applications for per-
forming rights, both amateur and professional, should be made
to:

Harvey Unna & Stephen Durbridge Ltd,
Authors' Agents,
14 Beaumont Mews,
Marylebone High Street,
London W1N 4HE.

Part One

RUNCIBLE STREET

A long row of simple terrace houses. A newsboy rides up on his bike, paper-bag over his shoulder. He pushes a folded newspaper into the letter-box of a house, then repeats the action two doors away, at the WESTONS' *house.*

THE WESTONS' HALLWAY

REG WESTON *comes out of the living-room, in shirtsleeves, and takes the paper out of the door.*

JOBY'S BEDROOM

Bright morning sunlight through the closed curtains. JOBY, *aged eleven, is in bed, his eyes closed.*

THE WESTONS' HALLWAY

NORAH WESTON *comes out of the living-room, wearing her best frock with a pinafore over it. She calls up the stairs.*

1 NORAH. Joby! Are you awake? Your breakfast's ready.

JOBY'S BEDROOM

2 JOBY. Righto!

Eyes open now, he stirs in the bed, then goes still again and the HEADMASTER'S *voice comes in:*

3 MR MORRISON. Audrey Adams . . .

CLASSROOM

MR MORRISON *is reading out the names of the County Minor Scholarship winners.*

4 MR MORRISON. . . . Geoffrey Broadhead, Edwin Arthur Dews, Barbara Fisher, Colin Laycock, John Edward Parker, [JOBY *bites his lip.*] Stanley Smith, Joseph Barry Weston.

JOBY's eyes light up.

SCHOOL CORRIDOR

Pupils make their way to the outer door, among them JOBY *and his friend* SNAP, *a loose-jointed, gangly lad with a tough cap of flaming ginger hair, and glasses.*

1 JOBY. Hard lines, Snap.

2 SNAP. Aw, it doesn't matter. I didn't want to go to Grammar School, anyway.

SCHOOL STEPS

As JOBY *and* SNAP *come out they pass* AUDREY ADAMS *huddled crying against the rail, with a* FRIEND *comforting her.*

3 JOBY. What's up with her?

4 AUDREY'S FRIEND. She's upset about her scholarship.

5 JOBY. She's passed, hasn't she?

6 AUDREY'S FRIEND. Yeh, but she says her mam an' dad won't let her go. She's to stop on here till she's fourteen, and then go to work.

JOBY and SNAP move across the playground.

7 JOBY. She's top in everything.

8 SNAP Yeh. Will your mam an' dad let *you* go?

9 JOBY. 'Course they will, man. [*Pause.*] Ey! They don't know I've passed yet. I'd better go an' tell 'em. [*Runs off.*] See you later, Snap.

THE WESTONS' HALLWAY

JOBY'S *mother appears and calls again.*

10 NORAH. Joby! Your breakfast's going cold. Come on, now. You know what a busy morning this is. I shan't call you again.

11 JOBY [*off*]. Okay.

JOBY'S BEDROOM

JOBY *is out of bed now. He draws back the curtain and looks out at the morning before reaching for his clothes.*

THE WESTONS' LIVING-ROOM

REG WESTON *is sitting at the table eating breakfast and drinking from a pint mug.* NORAH *is frying at the double gas-ring in the sink-corner.* JOBY *comes in.*

1   NORAH. Oh, you're here. Slow motion.

2   JOBY. I've got to get dressed properly, haven't I? You didn't want me to come down in me pyjamas, did you?

3   NORAH. We'll have a less of your answering back. Get to the table for your breakfast. We've a lot to do this morning. [*She puts a couple of sausages and some fried bread before him and pours him some tea.*] You haven't forgotten what day it is, have you?

4   JOBY. I know.

5   NORAH. Well, your Auntie Daisy'll be along any minute, and I want you to be ready when she gets here. There's your case to pack yet.

6   JOBY. What case?

7   NORAH. The case with your pyjamas and shirts and vests. Your Auntie Daisy'll wash your things through, but I don't want her to have to come rummaging through the drawers here every time you want a change of underclothes, so I'm sending you off with everything clean for a start.

8   JOBY. Can I take me gun and me bow an' arrer?

9   NORAH. You can't get your bow an' arrer into the case, so you mun come back for it one night when your dad's in.

    She is now taking JOBY's *things out of a sideboard drawer and putting them into a little attaché-case.*

10 JOBY. I can take me Dinky cars, though, can't I?

11 NORAH. Not all of 'em. Your Auntie Daisy doesn't want her house cluttering up with all manner of peg-meg. You'd better pick out one or two when you've had your breakfast. It's not as if I'm going away for six month.

12 JOBY. How long will they keep you in?

13 NORAH. Oh, a few days. It won't be long.

3

1   JOBY. Can I come and see you?

2   NORAH. Well, no. They don't let kiddies in. They have to keep the place quiet for them what's really poorly.

3   JOBY. I know how to be quiet. I can be as quiet as a mouse when I have to be.

4   NORAH. It's a rule they have. Anyway, I'll be back in no time at all, and your dad'll tell you all about it when he's been.

5   WESTON. I don't know why you wouldn't let your Daisy take you down this morning, 'stead o' me breaking me work and putting everybody about.

6   NORAH. Oh aye, folk can have mornings off for thick heads and out of idleness, but when you have to take your wife into hospital it's putting people about. It's your place to go.

7   WESTON. I just don't see any sense in chucking half a day's pay away. We're not millionaires.

8   NORAH. No, but you won't have me to keep for a week or two, so you'll be that much better off. You know, your trouble is 'at you just don't *want* to take me in.

9   WESTON. I don't like hospitals. They make me go all queer in me insides.

10 NORAH. You're a big soft lump. It's a pity they're not sticking the knife into *you*. That'd give you summat to get upset about.

11 JOBY. What knife? Are they going to cut you, Mam?

12 NORAH. I've got to have an operation, Joby; but it's nothing. They do it every day. I'll be right as rain and home again in no time.

JOBY is scared now and suddenly in tears.

13 JOBY. I don't want you to go.

His mother comes to him and presses his head into her side.

14 NORAH. There, there. There's no need for that.

15 JOBY. Don't go, Mam. Don't let 'em cut you open.

16 NORAH. Come on, Joby. Where's my big brave lad? I've got to

go, you see, because if I don't they can't make me better can they? And the sooner I go the quicker I'll be home again. There's nothing to worry about. Nothing at all. I'll be back again, all done and dusted, before you hardly know I've been away. [*She gives him her hankie.*] Dry your eyes before your Auntie Daisy comes. We don't want her to see you've been crying, do we?

JOBY *dries his tears and sniffs several times. There is a knock at the door.*

Hurry up and finish your breakfast. That sounds like your Auntie Daisy now.

But the knock comes again and NORAH *goes into the hallway. There is a murmur of voices before she comes back.*

That young Sidney Prendergast asking if you were in. I've sent him away.

2   JOBY. Snap? [*He gets up.*] I want to see him.
3   NORAH [*as he goes*]. We've enough to do without him hanging around.

RUNCIBLE STREET

As JOBY *runs out of the house,* SNAP *is mooching along some way off, hands in pockets, one foot in the gutter.*

4   JOBY. Oy, Snap!

SNAP *stops, turns, and retraces his steps a little way, then stops again, scuffing one toe in the gutter.*

I can't come out this morning.

5   SNAP. No, your mam said so.
6   JOBY. She's going into hospital today.
7   SNAP. Yeh, you told me before.
8   JOBY. An' I'm gunna stay at me Auntie Daisy's.
9   SNAP. Yeh, you told me.
10 JOBY. I might be able to call for you this aft.
11 SNAP. I shan't be in. I'm going to Leeds with me mam, shopping.

1 JOBY. Oh.

2 SNAP. We're gunna have us teas in Lewis's café.

3 JOBY. Oh—happen I'll come round and call for you tonight, then.

4 SNAP. I dunno what time we'll be back, but you can come round an' see, if you like.

5 JOBY. Okay.

SNAP *moves a few steps nearer.*

6 SNAP. Have you been roarin'?

7 JOBY. No, why?

8 SNAP. I thought you had.

9 JOBY. I got summat in me eye.

10 SNAP. Oh, I see.

JOBY *now sees, beyond* SNAP, *the figures of his* AUNTIE DAISY *and* COUSIN MONA *as they turn the corner and come along the street.*

11 JOBY. I can see me auntie coming, so I'll have to go back in now.

12 SNAP. Righto.

13 JOBY. I'll see you later, then.

14 SNAP. Yeh, see you later.

15 JOBY. If you're not in tonight I'll call for you in the morning.

16 SNAP. Righto.

17 JOBY. So long, then, Snap.

18 SNAP. So long, Joby.

SNAP *wanders off with a gangling eccentric gait towards the advancing figures of* JOBY'S AUNT *and* COUSIN, *as* JOBY *goes back into the house.*

THE WESTONS' LIVING-ROOM

JOBY *comes in.*

19 NORAH. Snap. Where ever did he pick up a name like that?

20 JOBY. It's his initials. Sidney, Norman, Arthur Prendergast. S-N-A-P. See?

21 NORAH. Sidney, Norman, Arthur . . . Well, that's a right

       mouthful, and no mistake. I make no wonder he's a bit dozy with a stringful o' names like that hanging round his neck.

2   JOBY. Snap's not dozy. He's got lots o' brains.

3   NORAH. He doesn't show much sign of 'em.

4   JOBY. He thinks a lot and writes it all down in books.

5   NORAH. Oh, does he?

6   JOBY. He says he's gunna get 'em published when he's older. He says he'd send 'em up now, only they wouldn't believe he'd written 'em if they found out he was only eleven, so he's waiting till he's sixteen and he'll send 'em up then.

7   NORAH. He's got big ideas.

8   JOBY. He's full of ideas, is Snap. He's got more ideas than anybody else I know.

9   NORAH. Well you'll meet a lot more boys when you get to Grammar School, so happen you won't want to see so much of him. An' you'd better be getting them Dinky cars sorted out if you're taking any with you. Your Auntie Daisy'll be here any time now.

10   JOBY. She's coming up the street now with our Mona.

       JOBY *moves to the cupboard to sort out his cars as* WESTON, *still at the table, shakes the newspaper.*

11   WESTON. That bloomin' 'Itler's at it again. Blethering about Poland now. He's getting a sight too big for his boots, that feller.

12   NORAH [*dryly*]. Aye, I reckon you an' your pal Mr Churchill 'ull have to teach him a lesson.

13   WESTON. It's about time somebody did. We'll have to fight him afore we've finished, or I know nowt about owt.

14   NORAH. It's time you were getting your collar and tie on.

15   WESTON [*glances at clock*]. It's only half past nine and we haven't to be there till half past ten.

16   NORAH. You never know how the buses'll be. And anyway, I don't like arriving at last minute.

       WESTON *gets up and, taking collar and tie from the sideboard top, begins to put them on in the mirror.* JOBY *sees his* MOTHER *stop for a moment and press one hand to the side of her breast, grimacing slightly. There is a knock and the front door opens.*

1 AUNT DAISY [*off*]. Anybody in?

AUNT DAISY enters, followed by her daughter MONA, *a rather lackadaisical young woman in her early twenties.*

2 NORAH. You're here, Daisy. Joby said he'd seen you coming up the street.

AUNT DAISY is out of breath. She sits down, gasping.

3 AUNT DAISY. By, but it's a pull.

4 NORAH. Well, there was no need for you to trail round, Daisy. Joby knows the way to your house.

5 AUNT DAISY. Oh, I thought I might be able to give you a hand with summat. You're sure you don't want me to come with you this morning?

6 NORAH. No, thanks all the same, Daisy. We'll manage.

7 WESTON. I've been telling her 'at she should ha' let you go with her when you first offered, Daisy. But she wouldn't have it.

8 NORAH. Now let's not start that all over again. You're taking me and that's the end of it.

9 WESTON. Aye, I've broken me work now, so we may as well let the arrangement stand. [*His tone changes to one of almost flirtatious banter as he speaks to* MONA.] Well, come on, Mona, sit yourself down, lass. It's free.

10 AUNT DAISY. Aye, sit down and don't get under t'feet. Mona.

MONA, who has been standing silently behind the table, moves to a chair.

11 NORAH. Could you drink a cup o' tea, Daisy? There's some left in the pot and it's fresh made.

12 AUNT DAISY. I can always manage a cup o' tea.

13 NORAH. What about you, Mona?

14 MONA. I'll have a drink o' pop, if you've got some.

NORAH and DAISY exchange a quick glance. There is something immature and unawakened about MONA, *and this preference for pop over tea is a small instance of it.*

1 NORAH. See if there's a bottle at the cellar-head, will you, Joby?

   JOBY *fetches a part-bottle of dandelion and burdock from the cellar-head as his mother rinses out a cup for* MONA.

2 NORAH. You don't mind a cup, do you, Mona? I'm saving on washing-up this morning.

3 AUNT DAISY. Our Mona 'ull see to t'washing-up for you.

4 NORAH. And you know what to do while I'm away, don't you, Mona? Just pop round in a morning and make your Uncle Reg's bed and wash up any pots he's left. You can run round with a duster as well, but there'll be nothing else for you to do. I've had a good clean down this week.

5 AUNT DAISY. You know I'd come and do it for you meself, Norah. Only it's such a pull up that street. And anyway, our Mona's as well doing that as hanging about at home.

6 NORAH. Didn't you get that new job you were going after, Mona?

7 MONA. Oh, I didn't fancy it.

8 AUNT DAISY. It's a job knowing what she does fancy.

9 WESTON. Well, wes'll manage, shan't we, Mona love? It'll give her a bit of practice for when she finds a chap.

10 AUNT DAISY. A chap? She's too slow to catch a cold, let alone a chap. There's that nice young feller Henry Musgrave three doors up from us. A right steady, clean-living, chapel-going chap. I'm sure he'd be interested if only she'd give him a bit of encouragement.

11 MONA [*mutters*]. Oh, Mam . . .

12 AUNT DAISY. Well, it's about time you were stirring yourself. You can't stop at home forever.

13 MONA. But I don't like Henry Musgrave.

14 AUNT DAISY. An' what's wrong with him, pray?

15 MONA. There's nothing wrong with him. I just don't want to court him, that's all.

1 AUNT DAISY. If you're waiting for Prince Charming to ride up on a white horse you'll be at home when you're seventy.

2 MONA. Oh, shurrup about it, Mam.

3 WESTON. Oh, she'll start courting all in good time, won't you Mona? When Mister Right come along, eh?

4 AUNT DAISY. Oh, aye. You encourage her. [*Pause.*] Is t'lad ready?

5 NORAH. All about. He's just sorting out a few of his Dinky cars.

JOBY begins to select, moving to one side a few of his special favourites.

I thought we could all walk down to the bus stop together.

6 AUNT DAISY [*snorts*]. Bus! Been me I'd ha' made Ted get me a taxi.

WESTON turns, brush and comb in hand.

7 WESTON. Nah look, if she wants a taxi she can have one. She's only got to say an' I'll go down to t'corner and ring up now.

8 AUNT DAISY. It's when you get things without asking 'at they mean the most, Reg.

9 WESTON. I can't read women's minds. How do I know when they . . .

10 NORAH. It's all right, it's all right. I never said anything about a taxi because I don't want one. The bus is good enough. I'm not bedridden yet.

11 AUNT DAISY. But you're poorly, Norah. Why else are they taking you in?

12 NORAH. Aye, I'm poorly all right. I've been poorly for some time, and carrying on as usual. I don't see why I should start acting like an invalid now.

13 WESTON. You can have a taxi if you want one. There's still time to ring up.

14 NORAH. I don't want one, Reg. I said I didn't want one and I don't. Now, for God's sake let's get cleared up and get off.

A LITTLE LANE

Evening of the same day. JOBY *and* SNAP *sit dangling their legs on a low wall.*

1   JOBY. An' this feller 'at come to me Auntie Daisy's chapel said they were setting fire to the churches in Spain. You can't say that's right, Snap.

2   SNAP. No, but the Fashists had filled the churches full o' guns and ammunition, an' that's not right either, is it?

3   JOBY. No, that's not right.

4   SNAP. An' the Fashists are the mates of the Nazzis in Germany, an' we don't like them, do we?

5   JOBY. No, we don't. Me dad says wes'll have to fight 'em before we've finished.

6   SNAP. So does me Uncle Bill. He says we should ha' stood up to 'em years ago when they started their tricks in Abyssinia.

7   JOBY. Who?

8   SNAP. The Eyeties.

9   JOBY. I thought we were talking about the Gerries.

10 SNAP. Well, the Eyeties are Fashists an' all. Them an' the Gerries helped the Fashists in Spain. Rotten dogs, the lot of 'em!

    SNAP *leaps down off the wall and begins to swing at thistles with his stick, capering about in a wild excess of energy and shouting.*

    Rotten dogs, dirty swine, stinking pigs!

11 JOBY. You don't half know some stuff, Snap.

12 SNAP. Ey! Guess who I saw in Leeds today. Go on, have a guess.

13 JOBY. Er . . . Gary Cooper.

14 SNAP. Aw, you're not guessing properly.

15 JOBY. Well, I dunno. Tell us.

16 SNAP. I'll give you a clue. Female.

17 JOBY. Er . . . Miss Roper.

18 SNAP. Naw. Not old Ropey. I wouldn't tell you I'd seen her.
    He brandishes his stick like a board-pointer and looks along his nose.

'Now, how many of you disgusting little boys have not scrubbed their hands this morning?'

2   JOBY. Ey, I say. When Ned Cooke walked out to the front that time with all his shirt lap hanging out at the back.

3   SNAP. An' all t'lasses were having fits.

4   JOBY. An' what did old Ropey say? Go on, Snap, you do it best. What did she say?

5   SNAP. 'We can see that your shirt needs washing, Cooke, without you showing us so much of it.'

6   JOBY. Yeh, that was it.

7   SNAP. An' Cookie just stood and looked at her an' dropped that terrific fart.

8   JOBY. Yeh!

They roll about, helpless with laughter at the memory.

9   SNAP. You haven't guessed who I saw yet.

10   JOBY. I can't guess.

11   SNAP. You can if you try.

12   JOBY. I can't be bothered.

13   SNAP. I won't tell you, then.

14   JOBY. Okay. I don't care.

15   SNAP. You would if you knew who it was.

16   JOBY. Well, if you won't tell me I won't know, so it doesn't matter.

17   SNAP. I'll give you another clue. She's somebody special.

18   JOBY. Well, if she wasn't special you wouldn't be making all this fuss about her, would you?

19   SNAP. She's somebody special to you. Somebody you like a right lot.

JOBY knows now, but cannot admit it to SNAP.

20   JOBY. Mae West.

21   SNAP. Aw, you're acting again.

JOBY gets down off the wall.

22   JOBY. Come on, let's buzz off somewhere else.

12

1 SNAP. I'll give you another clue. That's three. She wasn't born in England.

2 JOBY. Mae West.

3 SNAP. You're kidding on purpose. [*He grins.*] You've guessed and won't let on.

4 JOBY. How have I guessed?

5 SNAP. I can tell. You're blushin'. You know who it is because you're blushin'.

6 JOBY [*shouts*]. I tell you, I don't know. An' I don't care. An' if you don't stop acting about with your guessing I'm off home.

7 SNAP. Her initials are E.L.

8 JOBY. Elsie Lee, then.

9 SNAP. Who's Elsie Lee?

10 JOBY. One o' me aunties.

11 SNAP. I didn't know you had an Auntie Elsie.

12 JOBY. You don't know everything.

13 SNAP. You haven't got an Auntie Elsie.

14 JOBY. How do you know? I've just said I have, haven't I?

15 SNAP. I don't believe you.

16 JOBY. Well, *I* don't care. [*He strolls off.*] Come on, let's go somewhere.

17 SNAP [*falling in beside him*]. Where we going?

18 JOBY. I dunno.

19 SNAP. Have we time to go down t'Pastures?

20 JOBY. I dunno. Maybe it's too far. Me Auntie Daisy says I've to be in by nine.

21 SNAP. It must be nearly that now. [*Pause.*] Have I to tell you who it was?

22 JOBY. You can if you want. I'm not bothered. [*A silence.* JOBY *relents.*] Okay, tell us, then. [*Another silence.* JOBY *softens further.*] Was it Elsa Laedeker?

23 SNAP [*brightens*]. You knew all along, didn't you?

24 JOBY. I just thought about the initials and guessed.

1   SNAP. You knew before that.

>   JOBY *is furious with himself now, and, angry with* SNAP *for taking
>   advantage, he walks faster, kicking at loose stones.*

>   Wait on. [*He catches* JOBY *up.*] Wait on, Joby. Where you
>   going? [JOBY *does not answer.*] Don't get mad, Joby. [*He puts
>   his arm across* JOBY'S *shoulder and* JOBY *shrugs impatiently under its
>   weight.*] Come on, Joby. Don't get mad.

2   JOBY. I'm not mad.

3   SNAP. Y'are. I can see y'are.

4   JOBY. Is'll get mad if you keep on saying I'm mad.

5   SNAP. Okay, you're not mad.

6   JOBY. What if I am mad, anyway? What's it to do with you?

7   SNAP. I don't want you to be mad with me. We're mates,
     aren't we? [*A silence.*] Aren't we, Joby?

>   *In a moment* JOBY *reaches up and takes* SNAP'S *hand, pulling* SNAP'S
>   *arm round his shoulders.*

8   JOBY. Okay, we're mates.

>   SNAP *pulls free and begins to dance around, waving his stick and
>   singing a song:*

9   SNAP.
                         Will you come to Abyssinia
                         Will you come?
                         Will you bring your ammunition
                         and your gun?
                         Mussolini will be there
                         Shooting peanuts in the air.
                         Will you come to Abyssinia
                         Will you come?

>   JOBY *leans against a wall and goes into a brief daydream.*

A STREET

A tree-lined street of substantial houses. JOBY *stands on the corner as
a car turns in. In the passenger seat is* ELSA LAEDEKER *who smiles
sweetly and waves as she sees him.*

THE LANE

1 SNAP. Me dad says they're Jews.

2 JOBY. Who?

3 SNAP. The Laedekers. They haven't been here all that long
   but they live in a posh house and me dad says trust the
   Jews to do all right for themselves. Me Uncle Bill got
   mad and said me dad ought to go and join his pal
   Hitler and see what *he* was doing to the Jews. Me dad said
   everybody was busy calling Hitler names but look how
   he'd put Germany back on its feet and we could do with
   a bloke like him in England to shake things up. Then
   me Uncle Bill said he was talking like a bloody half-wit.
   We needed a shake-up all right but not putting hooli-
   gans in uniforms and letting them drag people out of
   their houses and kick 'em to death in the streets.
   Kicking who to death? me dad said, and me Uncle Bill
   said, the Jews. Oh, that lot, me dad said. It's about time
   they were put in their place. That started a real row. Me
   Uncle Bill said he wouldn't stop in the house another
   day and me dad said he was welcome to clear off any
   time he liked.

4 JOBY. He didn't go, though, did he?

5 SNAP. No, me mam came in and calmed 'em both down.

6 JOBY. But what *are* the Jews? That's what I'd like to know.

7 SNAP. They're the people who crucified Jesus Christ.

8 JOBY. Oh, I know *that*. But that was ages ago.

9 SNAP. Well, that's what they did and God drove them out of
   their country as a punishment and made them wander
   all over the world.

10 JOBY. And haven't they got a country now?

11 SNAP. No. They live all over the world, in other people's
   countries. But they still have a lot of their own rules,
   like going to the synagogue instead of church, and not
   eating meat on Fridays.

12 JOBY. No, that's the Catholics. The Macleods down our street
   are Catholics.

1 SNAP. Well, the Jews circumcise all their baby boys when they're born.

2 JOBY. I'm circumcised and I'm not a Jew.

3 SNAP. It's funny.

4 JOBY. I don't get it.

5 SNAP. Neither do I. [*Pause.*] Well, are we going down t'Pastures or are you going home?

6 JOBY. I dunno what time it is.

7 SNAP. Well, what say we walk down that way an' if we see a feller we'll ask him?

8 JOBY. Righto.

They move off. In a moment SNAP *starts the song again,* JOBY *joining in later and the two of them turning their walk into an exaggerated march.*

9 SNAP.

Will you come to Abyssinia
Will you come?
Will you bring your ammunition
and your gun?

10 BOTH.

Mussolini will be there
Shooting peanuts in the air.
Will you come to Abyssinia
Will you come?

RAILWAY BRIDGE

A rough, unsurfaced lane leading to a bridge carrying a railway spur, now disused, over the river. GUS WILSON, TOMMY MASTERMAN, *and a couple of other lads, all about the same age as, or a little older than,* JOBY *and* SNAP, *are hanging about there. As* JOBY *and* SNAP *come into sight of the gang,* SNAP *stops.*

11 SNAP. It's Gus Wilson and his lot.

12 JOBY. Yeh.

13 SNAP. They would be down there.

14 JOBY. What d'you wanna do?

1   SNAP. Well, it's getting late anyway. And you've got to be in early.

2   JOBY. Aye, but they've seen us now. They'll think we're running away or summat if we turn back.

3   SNAP. All right then. I'm not scared of Gus Wilson.

4   JOBY. Well, neither am I.

5   SNAP. Come on, then.

6   JOBY. Okay.

Assuming nonchalance, they stroll towards the bridge. Though they know everyone there, it is to the leader, GUS, that JOBY speaks first.

7   JOBY. How do, Gus.

8   GUS [*from the parapet*]. Now then, Joby. Where you off to?

9   JOBY. Oh, nowhere. Where you going?

10 GUS. Same place. I see you've got Foureyes with you. Ey, Foureyes, made any good lies up lately?

11 SNAP. What's up with you?

12 GUS. Nowt. What's up with you?

13 SNAP. Nowt.

14 GUS. Has your uncle shot any more planes down lately?

15 SNAP. I never said he had shot any planes down.

16 GUS. Garn, you did. You said he'd shot three planes down in Spain.

17 SNAP. I never said that.

18 GUS. Are you calling me a liar, Foureyes?

19 SNAP. You're calling me one.

20 GUS. That's different.

21 JOBY. What you been doing, then?

22 GUS. Aw, just hanging about. We've been watching a couple in that field. They've got no clothes on.

23 JOBY. Where? Which field?

24 GUS. Over there. [*Points with his stick.*] If you stand up here you can see 'em.

25 JOBY. Garn, you're kidding.

17

1   GUS. I'm telling you.

2   JOBY. Ah, you'll wait till I'm up there then push me.

3   GUS. Think I'm daft enough to push you with a drop like
    that?

4   JOBY. Well, I don't believe you, anyway.

5   GUS. It's right. In't it, lads?

6   TOMMY. Yeh, it's right, Joby.

7   JOBY. Okay, I'll have a look, then.

> *Challenged,* JOBY *climbs up on to the parapet and gingerly draws
> himself upright, his legs insubstantial, willing himself not to look
> down into the river and wary of some trick of* GUS'S.

8   GUS. Can't you see 'em?

9   JOBY. No, I can't.

10 GUS. Sure you're looking in the right place?

11 JOBY. I'm looking all over. I can't see owt.

> *There are muffled snorts of laughter from the gang.* JOBY *wonders
> what* GUS *is up to, but dare not look round quickly.*

C'mon, Gus. Stop kidding.

12 GUS. Stand on your toes, then you'll see better. [JOBY *forces
    himself on to his toes.*] Can't you see 'em now? Down in that
    far corner?

13 JOBY. You're having me on.

14 GUS. I tell you, there's a couple without clothes on. One of
    'em said summat as we come past.

15 JOBY. What did he say?

16 GUS. She.

17 JOBY. She then.

18 GUS. 'Moo.'

19 JOBY. Ah, cows.

> *He gets thankfully down.* GUS *and the gang are laughing.*

20 GUS. Ever been had.

21 JOBY. Very funny.

22 GUS. Why aren't you laughing, Foureyes?

1 SNAP. Because I don't feel like it.

2 GUS. Aw, you don't feel like it, eh?

3 JOBY. Lay off him, Gus.

4 GUS. I'm not doing owt to him, am I?

5 JOBY. No, but lay off. He's all right. He's my mate.

6 GUS. You can have him.

A MAN *with a greyhound at his heels crosses the bridge. He is shortish, in corduroy breeches, greasy cap and white silk muffler.*

7 JOBY. Ey, Mister, can you tell us the time, please?

8 THE MAN. Time you lot were in home.

As he goes on, SNAP *falls in behind him, walking in an exaggerated imitation of his loping gait that makes even* GUS *and the gang laugh.*

9 JOBY. Do you know what time it is, Gus?

10 GUS. Oh, it's early yet. You haven't to be in, have you?

11 JOBY. I'm stopping at me Auntie Daisy's. She said I'd to be in by nine.

12 GUS. Ah, well, it's struck nine long since.

13 JOBY. It never did.

14 GUS. I'm telling you. I heard the church clock.

15 JOBY. You can't hear the church clock right down here.

16 GUS. Oh, well, if you don't want to believe me . . .

17 JOBY. Happen I'd better push off, anyway. You coming, Snap?

18 GUS. What you stopping at your auntie's for, anyway?

19 JOBY. Me mam's gone into hospital.

20 GUS. Is she having a kid?

21 JOBY. Naw.

22 GUS. What's up with her, then?

23 JOBY. I dunno. She's got to have an operation.

24 GUS. Are they gunna cut her leg off?

25 JOBY. Naw, nowt like that.

26 GUS. How d'you know if you don't know what's up with her?

1   JOBY. Well, I know it's not her leg.

2   GUS. An auntie of mine went in an' they cut one of her tits
    off. She wears a balloon under her frock on one side
    now, so's it won't show.

    JOBY *begins to blush. He turns and begins to walk away, followed by*
    SNAP.

3   JOBY. So long, then, Gus.

    General farewells. A little later.

4   SNAP. What you blushing for, Joby?

5   JOBY. I'm not blushing.

6   SNAP. Y'are. You're as red as fire.

7   JOBY. I'm just hot, that's all.

8   SNAP. Was it what Gus said about his auntie?

9   JOBY [*angrily*]. I'm not blushing. Why don't you shurrup
    saying I'm blushing?

10 SNAP [*shrugs*]. Okay.

    They walk on in silence to the corner where they part.

11 JOBY. I'll see you tomorrow.

12 SNAP [*not looking*]. Aye, righto.

13 JOBY. Have I to come down in the morning?

14 SNAP. If you like.

15 JOBY. Have we to go down to Gibbert's Dyke an' see'f we can
    catch some newts?

16 SNAP. If you want to.

17 JOBY [*hesitates*]. If I tell you summat, Snap, will you promise
    not to tell anybody else?

18 SNAP. I can keep a secret.

19 JOBY. Cross your heart?

20 SNAP. Cross my heart.

21 JOBY. That what Gus was talking about—about his auntie. I
    think that's what they're going to do to me mam.

22 SNAP. I guessed it was.

23 JOBY. How did you guess?

1 SNAP. Oh, I just guessed.
2 JOBY. It's still a secret, though.
3 SNAP. Yeh, okay.
4 JOBY. See you, then.
5 SNAP. Okay. So long.

> *They part.* JOBY *walks thoughtfully along, looking back once at the departing* SNAP. *Then he suddenly breaks into a run.*

✳ ✳ ✳
Part Two

A SHOPPING STREET

JOBY *sees, across the street,* ELSA LAEDEKER *looking into a news-agent's window. He goes over and stands beside her, looking at her reflection and giving occasional covert sideways glances at her. He walks round and stands on the other side of her and she turns her head and gives him a casual glance in which there is neither recognition nor interest. Her* MOTHER *comes out of the shop and they walk away together, with* JOBY *looking after them.*
The sound of sporadic rifle fire and the tinkle of breaking glass comes in:

CLASSROOM

The room is in a state of siege. There are burning buildings outside. JOBY *and his fellow defenders relax below the level of the windows.* ELSA *looking adoringly at* JOBY, *passes him a reloaded rifle. He pats her hand reassuringly.*

1 JOBY. They're just sniping now. Don't worry.

ELSA *smiles with trust and adoration as* MR MORRISON *crawls across the room on his hands and knees.*

2 MR MORRISON. We've got through to Pontefract Barracks. Help's on its way.

3 JOBY. I doubt if they'll try another assault now, sir.

4 MR MORRISON. No, we've given them something they won't forget in a hurry. [*He lifts his head up and looks out.*] Good lord, look!

JOBY, *pulling himself up, sees that a* SOLDIER *in a strange uniform, has appeared at a window, a small object in his raised hand.*

5 MR MORRISON. It's a hand grenade!

6 JOBY. Leave him to me, sir.

JOBY *takes careful aim and shoots the* SOLDIER *as his arm goes back to throw the grenade. He falls out of sight and the sound of the grenade exploding is heard from outside.*

22

1   MR MORRISON. Good shot, Joby!

2   JOBY. It was nothing, sir.

He looks down into ELSA'S *adoring gaze.*

BARBER'S SHOP

A little saloon with only one of the two chairs in operation.

3   JOBY. What?

MR MANLEY, *the barber, stands over him, shaking the sheet.*

4   MR MANLEY. I said do you want your hair cutting or are you going to sit there all morning?

5   JOBY. Oh, sorry.

He gets up and crosses to the chair. MR MANLEY *sweeps the sheet round him and tucks it in.*

6   MR MANLEY. You were miles away, just then.

7   JOBY. I was just thinking about something.

8   MR MANLEY. Aye. What do you want, then—a tuppenny all off?

9   JOBY. Short back and sides, please, but leave the fringe alone 'cos I'm training it to go back.

10 MR MANLEY. In that case wes'll have to make you a parting an' put you a drop of cream on. [*He switches on the trimmer.*] How's your mam?

11 JOBY. She's in hospital.

12 MR MANLEY. Aye, I heard so. Has she had her operation yet?

13 JOBY. Yeh, day before yesterday.

14 MR MANLEY. Ah, well, you might be having her home soon, then.

15 JOBY. I hope so.

There are TWO OLD MEN, *chatting as they wait. One of them has a newspaper.*

16 FIRST OLD MAN. If we didn't stop him when he went into Czechoslovakia [*He can't pronounce it*]. why should we stop him over Poland?

1 SECOND OLD MAN. We've got a treaty with 'em this time.

2 FIRST OLD MAN. Poland? I don't even know where it is on t'map.

3 SECOND OLD MAN. Tha might soon enough find out, if things go on as they are.

JOBY resumes his fantasy.

CLASSROOM

The defenders are filing out. JOBY, *now with a bloodstained bandage round his head, walks with his arm across* ELSA'S *shoulders. An* ARMY OFFICER *stands in the doorway with* MR MORRISON *and salutes them.*

4 MR MORRISON. Well done! Well done, all of you!

The BARBER'S *voice comes in.*

5 MR MANLEY. He's at it again.

BARBER'S SHOP

6 JOBY. Eh?

7 MR MANLEY. I say you're at it again. Daydreaming. Do you want it from the bottle, or the spray?

8 JOBY. Er—the spray, please.

9 MR MANLEY. Right you are. [*He sprays* JOBY'S *hair liberally, then slicks it into place and whips off the sheet.*] There. Your girl friend'll hardly know you. [JOBY *gives him some coins.*] Ta. Tell your dad I hope your mam'll soon be up and about again.

10 JOBY [*exiting*]. Righto. Thanks, Mr Manley.

RUNCIBLE STREET

AGNES MACLEOD, *a girl of fifteen, is sitting on a wall with three boys paying court to her.* AGNES'S *sister* MOLLIE, *about twelve, is playing hopscotch on the pavement nearby as* JOBY *appears.*

11 MOLLIE. Hello, Joby.

12 JOBY. Hello.

13 MOLLIE. Has your mam come home from hospital yet?

1 JOBY. No, not yet.

2 MOLLIE. You're going to grammar school after the holidays, aren't you?

3 JOBY. Yeh.

4 MOLLIE. Are you glad?

5 JOBY. Yeh! I want to go.

6 MOLLIE. I want to leave school soon as I can and get a job, like our kid.

7 JOBY. Where's she working?

8 MOLLIE. She starts at Hanson's on Monday.

9 JOBY. Well, I've got to go now.

10 MOLLIE. Righto. Hope your mam's home soon.

JOBY goes on towards his house.

11 JOBY. Yeh. Thanks.

MOLLIE watches her sister knowingly as she flirts with the boys.

THE WESTONS' LIVING-ROOM

JOBY enters. The morning newspaper lies on the table. JOBY opens it and extracts his weekly copy of 'The Hotspur'. As he opens that he thinks he hears voices from upstairs. He looks up, then goes back to the hall door and calls upstairs.

12 JOBY. Mona! Are you there?

MONA comes down and enters, one hand touching her hair.

13 MONA. What are you doing here, Joby?

14 JOBY. I came to fetch me comic. [*As she approaches.*] Have you been cleaning upstairs?

15 MONA. I was talking to your dad.

16 JOBY. Isn't he at work?

17 MONA. He didn't go. He wasn't feeling well.

18 JOBY. Is he in bed?

19 MONA. He's getting up now.

MONA'S cheeks are rather red and she appears a little flustered and out of breath.

1 JOBY. What's wrong with him?

2 MONA. He says it's his stomach 'at's upset. I didn't know what
   he was going to do for his dinner; whether he wanted
   me to fetch him some fish and chips.

3 JOBY. Me Auntie Daisy's given me some money to get some
   fish and chips for us.

4 MONA. Yes. Well, your dad says he can manage.

   WESTON *enters, buttoning his shirt.*

5 WESTON. Hello, Joby. What you doing here?

6 JOBY. I came to get me comic.

7 WESTON. Oh, aye?

8 JOBY. Our Mona says you're feeling poorly.

9 WESTON. Oh, it's all right, lad. Me insides are a bit upset, that's
   all. You've had your hair cut, I see.

10 JOBY. Me Auntie Daisy made me go. Mr Manley was asking
   about me mam.

11 MONA. I'll be walking round home.

12 WESTON. Aye, thanks, Mona. See you later, love. [MONA *leaves.*]
   Is your Auntie Daisy looking after you all right?

13 JOBY. Yeh, all right. I'd rather be at home, though.

14 WESTON. It won't be long now.

15 JOBY. Will me mam be coming home soon?

16 WESTON. They just have to keep an eye on her for a bit.

17 JOBY. Is she still poorly?

18 WESTON. The doctors are very pleased with her.

19 JOBY. I'd better be going. I've to call for some fish and chips.

20 WESTON. Aye, all right. [*As* JOBY *reaches the door,* WESTON *calls him
   back.*] I say, Joby . . . it might be best if you didn't say owt
   to your auntie about me being off work today. You
   know what a fussy body she is.

21 JOBY. All right.

22 WESTON. Will you tell our Mona?

23 JOBY. Righto.

   WESTON *feels in his pocket.*

26

1   WESTON. Here, there's a bob for your spend.

2   JOBY. Ooh, ta! So long, then.

3   WESTON. So long, Joby.

    JOBY *exits*.

AUNT DAISY'S SCULLERY

JOBY, without trousers, and his shirt tucked between his legs, is standing in a bowl of water. He rubs at his knees with a soapy flannel.

4   AUNT DAISY. Get 'em scrubbed, Joby. Get 'em properly clean. By the livin' . . . I could grow a stone o' taties in the muck on your legs.

5   JOBY [*sullenly*]. I'm gunna be late for t'pictures.

6   AUNT DAISY. You will be if you don't use some elbow grease. Get on with it, lad.

    MONA *comes in with some dirty dishes.*

7   MONA. Here, I'll get 'em clean.

    She takes a scrubbing brush, applies water and soap, and begins to attack JOBY'S *legs till he howls in protest.*

8   JOBY. Here, steady on, our Mona, Don't be so rough.

9   MONA. I shall have to be rough to shift this lot. It's grained in. You look as if you've done a shift down t'pit. And you've got tidemarks where your trousers come.

    The brush moves up the tender skin of JOBY'S *thighs.*

10   JOBY. That's far enough. I'm not having a bath.

11   MONA. What's wrong? Are you bashful? [*She pretends to tweak at* JOBY'S *shirt.*] What you got hiddied under there?

12   JOBY. Lay off. Give over.

13   AUNT DAISY [*primly*]. That'll do, Mona. Are they clean now? [*Leans over and looks.*] That's better. Your mam'd never forgive me if I let you go out looking like somebody from Foundry Yard.

A CINEMA

The circle, filled with the noisy young clients for the Saturday matinée. JOBY *appears and looks round.* SNAP *stands up and waves to him.* JOBY *pushes along the row and takes the next seat.*

1 SNAP. Good job I saved you a seat. I thought you weren't coming.

2 JOBY. Aw, it was me Auntie Daisy.

On the row behind are GUS WILSON *and friends, including* TOMMY MASTERMAN.

3 GUS. Ey, here's Foureyes. You'd better keep your nut down when the picture starts, kid.

4 SNAP. You can see, can't you?

5 GUS. If I can't I'll bray your head down into your shoulders, like this.

He puts one clenched hand on top of SNAP'S *head and beats on it with the other.* SNAP *squirms out of the way.*

6 SNAP. Why can't you leave people alone, Gus Wilson?

7 GUS. What do you mean by that?

8 SNAP. You're allus making trouble.

9 GUS. Oh, am I? I'd better make some for you, then.

JOBY turns round.

10 JOBY. Look, lay off, Gus, will you?

11 GUS. I will if I want to.

12 JOBY. Well want to. We've paid to come in, so let us alone.

13 GUS. I'm not doing owt to you.

14 JOBY. You're messing about with Snap.

15 GUS. What's that got to do with you?

16 JOBY. A lot.

17 GUS. Oh, has it?

18 JOBY. Aye, it has. So just remember.

19 GUS. Oh, Joby Weston's a tough guy. I'd better be careful else he'll bash me up.

But GUS, *not looking for a fight now, lets* JOBY *turn away.* JOBY *breaks a bar of toffee and gives half to* SNAP.

20 JOBY. Here, Snap.

1   SNAP. Ooh, ta!

Behind them GUS *takes aim with a rubber band catapult and fires a paper pellet. A few rows down a boy claps his hand to his neck and looks round. But* GUS *is all innocence. As soon as the boy turns away* GUS *fires again. The boy rears to his feet and turns in a fury.*

2   THE BOY. Some'dy's shooting pellets back there. Gi' over, will you!

The house lights go down and on to the screen come slides of local advertisers. The ATTENDANT, *a little elderly man, moves about with his torch.*

3   ATTENDANT. Settle down now. Let's have some hush! [*He dabs at his cheek as a pellet strikes him, and flashes his torch into the audience.*] Who's firing pellets? Come on, which of you is it? [*No reply.*] I can put you all out, y'know. And don't think I won't.

4   GUS. Ah, go shove your head up a drainpipe, you daft old keff.

5   ATTENDANT. Who said that? [*The torch beam plays about and falls on* JOBY, *who is grinning broadly.*] You there. Was it you?

6   JOBY. Who, me?

7   ATTENDANT. Yes, you. Come on out here.

8   JOBY. I haven't done owt.

9   ATTENDANT. Come on out before I come in and fetch you.

10 JOBY. Oh, cripes! [GUS *sniggers as* JOBY *squeezes out to the aisle.*] I don't know what you're on about.

11 ATTENDANT. We'll see about that.

He takes JOBY's *arm and leads him to the door.*

12 JOBY. Where we going?

13 ATTENDANT. You're going out.

14 JOBY. But I'm gunna miss the serial. It's the last chapter.

15 ATTENDANT. You should have thought about that before.

16 JOBY. Look, I know who it was but it wasn't me.

17 ATTENDANT. Who was it, then?

18 JOBY. I can't split, can I?

29

1   ATTENDANT. No, because it was you.

2   JOBY. Why don't you ask the lad I was with? He'll tell you it wasn't me.

3   ATTENDANT. Aw, he'll stick up for you. [*Opens the door.*] Anyway, I can't mess about with you all afternoon, so you can get off home.

4   JOBY. You mean I really can't go back in?

5   ATTENDANT. No, you can't. And you won't get in next week, either, if I see you first. [*He pushes* JOBY *through the door on to the stairs*]. Now clear off.

6   JOBY. I hope you get another pellet in your earhole.

7   ATTENDANT [*calls after him*]. Be off with you, you cheeky young devil, before I clatter your face!

OUTSIDE THE CINEMA

The street is quiet. JOBY *comes out of the cinema and lingers for a frustrated look at the stills in the case on the wall.* MOLLIE MACLEOD *comes round the corner.*

8   MOLLIE. Hello, Joby. Why aren't you in the pictures?

9   JOBY. Didn't feel like it today. What are you doing?

10   MOLLIE. I'm just off for a walk.

11   JOBY. Where to?

12   MOLLIE. Just down to the railway. Want to come?

13   JOBY [*shrugs*]. Might as well.

14   MOLLIE. Come on, then.

JOBY *slouches moodily after* MOLLIE, *who turns after a little way.*

Come on, then, if you're coming.

RAILWAY BRIDGE

JOBY *and* MOLLIE *appear.*

15   JOBY. You're not going right down on the riverside, are you?

16   MOLLIE. No—we'll soon be there.

17   JOBY. Where?

18   MOLLIE. Where I want to be.

1 JOBY. I thought you were just going for a walk.

2 MOLLIE. I'm looking for something as well.

3 JOBY. Is it summat you've lost?

4 MOLLIE. Well, no. I'm looking for some*body*, really.

5 JOBY. Who, then?

6 MOLLIE. Our kid.

7 JOBY. Your Agnes?

8 MOLLIE. Yeh.

9 JOBY. What's she doing down here?

10 MOLLIE. That's what I want to find out.

They have now come to a small wood into which MOLLIE *leads* JOBY. *After a time she bids him be silent.*

Shurrup now. Don't talk. Wait here. I'll be back in a tick.

She leaves him and moves into the trees. He waits, wondering. In a while she reappears and beckons him to her, a finger to her lips. He follows her until she suddenly crouches and makes him follow suit. She points and he follows her gesture, in a moment making out the recumbent form of AGNES MACLEOD *with a boy on top of her. Her skirt is pulled back and she is holding the boy with her knees.* JOBY *watches, fascinated, until* MOLLIE *touches his arm and beckons him away. They go quietly back up to the path and walk along to a meadow on the edge of the wood.*

I knew I'd find her.

11 JOBY. Why'd you want to trail all this way down here if you knew where she was?

12 MOLLIE. I wanted to make sure. She'll have to give me a tanner now so's I won't tell me mam.

13 JOBY. Suppose she gives you a clout for spying on her?

14 MOLLIE. She daren't do that. She knows I'll tell me mam, and then she'll get a leathering. She's been told to leave the lads alone but she can't keep away from 'em.

15 JOBY. Have you had any money out of her before?

16 MOLLIE. Many a time. 'Fact, I'm thinking of putting the price up to a bob. She'll have more money now she's starting

working. [*A sidelong look.*] Could you see what they were
doing?

2   JOBY. Kissing one another.

3   MOLLIE. Is that all?

JOBY *plucks at the grass, his face reddening.*

4   JOBY. I dunno.

5   MOLLIE. I'll bet you don't know the difference between men
and women.

6   JOBY. 'Course I do.

7   MOLLIE. What is it, then?

8   JOBY. Well . . . well, women have longer hair.

MOLLIE *hoots with laughter.*

9   MOLLIE. Longer hair! Is that all, then?

10 JOBY. No, there's other things.

11 MOLLIE. What other things?

12 JOBY. I don't know the words.

13 MOLLIE. Joby . . .

14 JOBY. What?

15 MOLLIE. If I show you will you show me?

16 JOBY. What for?

17 MOLLIE. You'd like to know, wouldn't you?

18 JOBY. Mebbe.

19 MOLLIE. You're blushing.

20 JOBY. Well, what if I am?

21 MOLLIE. You're scared, that's why.

22 JOBY. I'm not scared. I got thrown out of the pictures this
afternoon.

23 MOLLIE. What for?

24 JOBY. Shooting pellets at the attendant.

MOLLIE *appears unimpressed.*

25 MOLLIE. I'll go first if you go second.

26 JOBY. What if somebody comes?

1 MOLLIE. Nobody can see us here. Come on, then, will you promise?

2 JOBY. I'm thinking about it.

RAILWAY BRIDGE

JOBY *appears, running towards the town.*

OUTSIDE THE CINEMA

The matinée over, the audience pours into the street, some of the younger ones firing imaginary guns and slapping their own backsides as they run, their imaginations still in the grip of the film. JOBY *crosses the road as* SNAP *appears.*

3 SNAP. Where you been, Joby?

4 JOBY. Just walking around. Was it a good show?

5 SNAP. Yeh, right good. Hard lines you getting sent out like that.

6 JOBY. I told him it wasn't me but he wouldn't believe me. Did Gus make any more trouble?

7 SNAP. Naw.

8 JOBY. No, he's too crafty to give the game away like that.

9 SNAP. He was on to me a bit, flicking me ear.

10 JOBY. Aye, he would be.

Somebody bumps into JOBY *and sends him reeling into* SNAP, *who holds him up.*

Here, steady on, can't you?

He turns to see the false innocence on GUS'S *face.*

11 GUS. Oh, sorry, Joby.

12 JOBY. What d'you mean 'sorry'? You did that on purpose.

13 GUS. I never did.

14 JOBY. No, and I don't suppose you let me take the blame and get chucked out of the pictures, either?

15 GUS. It's not my fault if you get chucked out.

16 JOBY. It is when it should ha' been you.

17 GUS. Why me, then?

33

1 JOBY. Because you shot the pellet and gave him the cheek, but he picked on me instead.

2 GUS. Hard lines, then.

3 JOBY. Yeh, hard lines. You won't find that big shot Gus Wilson owning up to what he's done. He'd rather let some'dy else take the blame.

SNAP plucks at his sleeve.

4 SNAP. Come on, Joby. Let's go.

5 JOBY. You buzz off if you want to. I'm talking to Big Shot Wilson.

6 GUS. You wanna be careful who you're calling.

7 JOBY. Why?

8 GUS. Else you might get bashed.

9 JOBY. Fetch your army and start bashing.

10 GUS. I don't need no army to bash you, Weston.

He pushes at JOBY's shoulder. JOBY, losing his temper, swings and strikes GUS on the cheek, then dances back with his fists at the ready. Immediately a ring is formed for the contest. GUS's aim is more accurate and tears spring to JOBY's eyes. He goes at GUS with a flail of fists, then, as he retires again, GUS rushes him. At this moment the cinema ATTENDANT breaks into the ring and grabs them both and holds them apart.

11 ATTENDANT. That's enough o' that. Stop it now! [*He looks at* JOBY.] You causing trouble again, eh? I thought I told you to clear off home long since?

12 JOBY. You don't own the street, do you?

13 ATTENDANT. I'll tell you what, though. I own a good clout on the earhole 'at I'll give you in a minute. [*He pushes them both away.*] Now get off home, the lot of you. [*JOBY finds himself walking away at GUS's side.*] And don't forget what I told you. You've no need to come back next week, 'cos you won't get in.

JOBY swings round and calls after him.

14 JOBY. Aw, go and boil your fat head, you silly old bugger!

Turning back he cannons into a well-dressed woman who stands and

34

looks after him with a shocked face. They turn the corner. SNAP *has gone.*

1 TOMMY. Your mate seems to have cleared off.

2 JOBY. He won't be far away.

3 TOMMY. I wouldn't call *him* a mate. He buzzes off as soon as there's trouble.

4 JOBY. Well he doesn't go round making it for other people. And anyway, nobody's asking what you think.

5 TOMMY. Okay, if you want it like that.

6 JOBY. Yeh, I do.

7 GUS. Don't forget we've a scrap to finish.

8 JOBY. Any time you like.

He leaves them and walks off.

THE WESTONS' LIVING-ROOM

WESTON *is making his tea. He has laid the table with the bare necessities and while the kettle comes to the boil is opening a tin of salmon.* JOBY *comes in moodily, hands in pockets.*

9 JOBY. Hello, Dad.

10 WESTON. Hello, Joby. How you doing?

11 JOBY. Oh, not bad. [*Pause.*] Is your stomach better?

12 WESTON. What? Oh, aye, it's all right now.

13 JOBY. Have you been to see me mam?

14 WESTON. Yes. She's sitting up and taking notice now. She said to tell you to be a good lad and she won't be long as she's home.

WESTON *pushes the salmon out on to a plate and pours boiling water into the teapot.*

15 JOBY. I wish I could go and see her.

16 WESTON. Aye, but it's against the rules, lad. [*Pause.*] Have you had your tea, then?

17 JOBY. No.

18 WESTON. Your Auntie Daisy'll have it ready for you, won't she?

1 JOBY. Can't I stop and have me tea with you?

2 WESTON. You don't want to put your auntie about, you know. We don't want to offend her.

3 JOBY. I'd rather stop here for it.

4 WESTON [*hesitates*]. Oh, well, I reckon it'll be all right for once. Get yourself some tackle out. [*As* JOBY *gets knife and fork and mug* WESTON *pours from the teapot.*] Damnation, I've not put any tea in. I'll forget me own name next.

He pours the water back into the kettle to reboil. JOBY *scrapes some of the salmon on to his plate.*

5 JOBY [*after a silence*]. I got thrown out of the pictures this aft., Dad.

6 WESTON. Oh, aye?

7 JOBY. It wasn't my fault, though. I wasn't doing owt. It was Gus Wilson, y'see. He was firing pellets with a rubber band and the attendant thought it was me. He wouldn't take any notice of what I said.

8 WESTON. You'll have to behave yourself, else they'll be stopping you going.

9 JOBY. He says I can't go any more now. And it wasn't me at all, it was Gus Wilson.

10 WESTON. Have you got enough there?

11 JOBY. Yeh, thanks.

WESTON *scrapes the rest of the salmon on to his own plate.*

12 WESTON. Very tasty now and then, a bit of salmon. Been a pity to open that big tin just for me, though.

They eat in silence for a while, JOBY *wondering at his father's pre-occupation.*

13 JOBY. Are you worried about summat, Dad?

14 WESTON. Well, I have summat on me mind a bit.

15 JOBY. Is it about me mam?

16 WESTON. No . . . it's about a little job at work, that's all.

Another silence.

17 JOBY. Is there a cricket match down in t'field tonight?

36

1   WESTON. I don't know. Why?

2   JOBY. I thought you might be going to watch it.

3   WESTON. I can't tonight. I've got to go and pay me sick-club
    dues.

    Another silence.

4   JOBY. Dad.

5   WESTON. Eh?

6   JOBY. About the pictures. I was wondering. If you went to see
    that attendant and told him it wasn't me what made the
    trouble, happen they'd let me in next week.

7   WESTON. Oh, I shouldn't worry about that. It'll all come out
    in t'wash. [*Pause.*] You'd better get on with your tea and
    go and let your Auntie Daisy know where you are, else
    she'll be wondering.

RUNCIBLE STREET

JOBY *comes out of the house and mopes moodily off the other way.*

THE TOWN

As JOBY *comes to a corner a bus goes by. He half registers that it has
a Cressley destination on it as it stops a little way off. As it begins to
move again he runs for it and jumps on.*

OUTSIDE THE HOSPITAL

A forbidding looking building on a hill. JOBY *walks warily up the
drive from the road, standing well back at one point as an ambulance
passes him, going into the town. There seems to be no one about to
question him as he approaches the main entrance, steels himself, and
goes in.*

INSIDE THE HOSPITAL

JOBY *is in a big echoing waiting-hall. He stands back round a corner as
two nurses walk through on the far side, soft laughter echoing up. He
ventures farther in and looks along a corridor leading into the heart of
the building. He is caught like that by a middle-aged* NURSING
SISTER *who comes suddenly on him, making him start violently as she
speaks.*

1   SISTER. Now, young man, what do *you* want?

2   JOBY [*stammers*]. I was looking for me mother.

3   SISTER. Are you with her?

4   JOBY. No, I'm on me own.

5   SISTER. Have you been sent here for treatment? Is there
      something wrong with you?

6   JOBY. No, I'm looking for me mam.

7   SISTER. Is your mother a patient here?

8   JOBY. Yes, she's inside.

9   SISTER. Ah, I see. Well, I'm afraid you can't see her. Visiting
      hours are over, and little boys aren't allowed in anyway.
      What's her name?

10 JOBY. Mrs Weston. I wanted to find out how she was getting
      on, so I came up.

11 SISTER. Hasn't anybody visited her?

12 JOBY. Me dad comes.

13 SISTER. Hasn't he told you how she is?

14 JOBY. He says she's all right. But I wanted to find out for
      meself.

15 SISTER [*hesitates*]. You wait here. Don't go wandering off.

      She walks away round a corner. JOBY *waits, wondering what she is
      going to do. He moves back out of sight as a nursing orderly pushes a
      stretcher by with a prone figure on it.*
      Suddenly an AMBULANCE MAN *comes upon him. A hand falls on*
      JOBY'S *shoulder. He whirls round and sees a flash of uniform which he
      instantly translates into a symbol of unrelenting authority. He twists
      free and runs for the door hearing a vague shout from behind him.*

      OUTSIDE THE HOSPITAL

      JOBY *comes rushing out and runs down the drive. Only when he has
      cleared the grounds does he stop and lean against a wall, pressing his
      arms across his pounding chest. He begins to cry. Taking a few paces,
      then stopping to hide his face in his arms, he makes his way down into
      the town. The street is deserted.*

Part Three

A SMALL CHAPEL   Sunday morning

It is the day after JOBY'S *attempt to see his mother.* JOBY *sits between* AUNT DAISY *and* COUSIN MONA, *all in their Sunday best. The congregation is singing the hymn 'Now Thank We All Our God'.*

1   PREACHER. I shall take as my text in these troubled days St Matthew, Chapter Five, verses 8 and 9. 'Blessed are the pure in heart; for they shall see God. Blessed are the peacemakers: for they shall be called the children of God'.

AUNT DAISY sits smugly expectant, MONA *vacuous,* JOBY *resigned to boredom.*

AUNT DAISY'S LIVING-ROOM

JOBY'S *father is now present. They are finishing their Sunday lunch.*

2   WESTON. Well he come and asked if he could have his tea with me, Daisy, and I sent him round here straight after, to tell you where he'd been.

3   AUNT DAISY. It took him a long time to get here. It was nearly ten o'clock by the time he walked in.

4   WESTON. And where the hummer had you been to till that time?

5   JOBY. Oh, just hanging about.

6   WESTON. Didn't I tell you to come straight round here and tell your Auntie Daisy where you'd been?

7   JOBY. Yes.

8   WESTON. And why didn't you, then?

9   JOBY. I forgot.

10   AUNT DAISY. Aye, with our Mona out searching the streets for him, and me sitting here wondering if he'd had an accident, or summat.

11   WESTON. You'd better behave yourself in future. I've a good

39

mind to give you a hiding. It's bad enough your mam being away without you upsetting your Auntie Daisy when she's doing all she can to help us. Y'hear what I'm saying?

2 JOBY. Yes.

3 WESTON. Well just think on, 'else you'll be feeling the flat of my hand.

4 MONA. I think he's worried about his mam. Aren't you, Joby?

5 WESTON. What's he want to be worried about her for? I've told him she's going on all right. More likely she'll be worried about him when she gets to know what he's been up to.

6 JOBY. You won't tell her, Dad, will you?

7 WESTON. What have I to tell her if she asks me if you've been a good lad?

8 JOBY. I don't want her to get upset.

9 WESTON. Why didn't you think of that before, eh?

10 JOBY. Are you going to see her this afternoon?

11 WESTON. I am. And your Auntie Daisy's going with me.

12 JOBY. If I write her a letter will you give it to her for me?

13 WESTON. All right.

14 JOBY. Then she might write me one back.

15 WESTON. Aye, happen so.

16 AUNT DAISY. We'd better be getting a move on if we're going up there. We don't want to be late.

17 MONA. I'll see to the washing-up.

18 WESTON. You wash and I'll dry. There's no need to rush. There's a bus at two 'at'll get us there in time.

19 AUNT DAISY. Oh, well, in that case I'll have a lie-down for ten minutes. I do like a lie-down on a Sunday afternoon.

She exits to stairs.

20 JOBY. Have you got some paper, Mona?

MONA *gets a cheap pad, envelope and pencil from the sideboard drawer.*

1 MONA. Here y'are.

2 JOBY. Ta.

He begins to compose his letter at a corner of the table as MONA *and his* FATHER *take the dishes into the kitchen. Once he has decided what to put he writes with a firm hand, without corrections. He slips the sheet into the envelope and goes towards the kitchen to give it to his father. The door is ajar. He stops and peers through the gap as he hears a curious exclamation, something between a gasp and a giggle, from* MONA.

3 MONA [*off*]. Look, behave yourself. You'll get us both into bother. Look, me mam'll be down any time, and there's Joby just next door.

4 WESTON. We're all right for a minute. What're you scared of?

They are standing very close together. JOBY *sees his father embrace* MONA *and kiss her on the mouth. In a moment she pushes him away.*

5 MONA. Give it up, now. Don't be so daft.

JOBY retreats and opens his comic. MONA *comes through.*

Oh, have you finished your letter, then? That didn't take long.

6 JOBY. It's only a short one.

7 MONA. I hope there's no spelling mistakes in it.

8 JOBY. I'm a good speller. I'm nearly allus at the top in spelling.

9 MONA. I never could spell. And I don't like writing letters. You can never say things properly in a letter.

10 JOBY. Where's me dad?

11 MONA. He's just having a wash under the tap. Do you want to go down on the bus with me mam and your dad and have a walk round the park while they're in the hospital?

12 JOBY. I thought me Auntie Daisy said I'd to go to Sunday School?

13 MONA. Oh, yeh, I'd forgotten. You'd better go, then. You won't get a prize if you keep missing.

14 JOBY. I don't want to go, though.

WESTON comes in.

1   WESTON. What 're you saying you don't want to do?

He is rubbing towel fluff off his face.

2   MONA. Here, you've missed some.

She pulls fluff off his cheek.

3   WESTON. New towels . . . What you saying you don't want to
     do? It's about time you did as you were told, never mind
     saying what you want and don't want. Have you got
     that letter done?

JOBY hands it to him.

4   JOBY. You won't forget to give it to her, will you? And ask
     her to write me one back?

5   WESTON. I don't know as she'll have time to be writing letters,
     with visitors there. Happen she'll write one when we've
     gone, and send it on next time.

6   JOBY. Ask her if she knows when she's coming home.

7   WESTON. I'll see if she's got to know owt else about it. Get
     yourself off and get ready for Sunday School.

A QUIET STREET

*JOBY rounds a corner and stops on seeing GUS and TOMMY sitting on
a wall and taking alternate swings from a big bottle of lemonade.
Their clothes make no concession to the sabbath and JOBY, turned out
neat in Sunday best, feels uneasy at the prospect of meeting them.
There is also the matter of yesterday's unfinished fight with GUS. But
GUS, as he approaches, greets him amiably enough.*

8   GUS. Hi, Joby. Where you off to?

9   JOBY. Sunday School.

10   GUS. What for?

11   JOBY. 'Cos I have to.

12   GUS. Seen that mate of yours, Snap, lately?

13   JOBY. I saw him yesterday, at the pictures.

14   GUS. Aw, when he buzzed off an' left you, you mean. Haven't
      you heard about his uncle?

1 JOBY. No. What about him?

2 GUS. He's hung hisself.

3 JOBY. You're kidding.

4 TOMMY. 'Strue, Joby.

5 GUS. Cross me heart. He hung hisself last night in t'lav., with his braces.

6 JOBY. Well . . . what did he want to do that for?

7 GUS. How do I know? Mebbe he left a note and they'll find out from that.

8 TOMMY. They say it wa' Snap 'at found him.

9 GUS. Aye, he went out for a pee an' when he opened the lav. door there he was, hanging up by his braces. [*He offers the bottle to* JOBY.] Wanna swig?

10 JOBY [*shakes his head*]. Is'll have to go. Me dad and me Auntie Daisy'll be coming on here in a minute, and I'm supposed to be at Sunday School.

11 GUS. We'll walk on with you. [*He hands the bottle to* TOMMY *to carry and they walk with* JOBY *towards the middle of the village.*] I wouldn't hang meself if I wanted to do meself in. Not with me braces, anyway. When they hang a murderer they have a big knot in a rope and that breaks his neck as soon as he drops through the trap. You can't do that with braces. You'd just throttle yourself, ever so slow.

12 TOMMY. I'd chuck meself under a train.

13 GUS. An' be chopped into little bits?

14 TOMMY. It's quick, anyway.

15 GUS. Shooting yerself's best. [*Points two fingers at the side of his head.*] Just pull the trigger and it's all over. Bang!

16 TOMMY. What if you can't get a gun?

17 GUS. Well, I'd jump off a high building, like Blackpool Tower.

18 TOMMY. What about drownding?

19 GUS. Naw, you might change your mind and try to swim out.

20 TOMMY. What about taking a lot of aspirins afore you go to bed? Then you'd just die in your sleep.

1   GUS. Time to change your mind again.

2   TOMMY. Well, there's gassing yourself.

3   GUS. Yeh, that's not bad. Hate the stink of gas, though.

4   TOMMY. Some folk cut their throats from ear to ear.

5   GUS. Mebbe you wouldn't have the guts to hurt yourself like that.

6   TOMMY. You need guts to commit suicide at all.

7   GUS. Naw, it's the cowards's way out.

8   JOBY. I don't think Snap's uncle was a coward.

9   GUS. Why'd he kill hisself, then?

10 JOBY. Well, he went to fight in Spain, didn't he? He'd no need to do that.

11 GUS. Mebbe he didn't know how rough it was gunna be.

12 JOBY. Nobody knows why he killed hisself either, do they?

13 GUS. Not unless he wrote a letter. Lots o' people write letters when they do theirselves in.

14 JOBY. Not all of 'em.

15 GUS. No, but most of 'em.

They have come to where JOBY *can see the chapel. There is nobody about.*

16 JOBY. They've all gone in. Is'll be late.

17 GUS. Why don't you come with us instead?

18 JOBY. Where you going?

19 GUS. Down the park in Cressley. There'll be a band playing this aft.

20 JOBY. Is'll have to make sure I'm back in good time, if I do.

21 GUS. We're off to catch a bus now. [*He and* TOMMY *move off,* GUS *looking back after a few yards.*] Are you coming, then?

JOBY hesitates for a second longer, looking across once more at the chapel.

22 JOBY. Aye, wait on, then.

He jogs after them and catches them up.

AUNT DAISY'S SCULLERY

JOBY enters as AUNT DAISY *comes through from the living-room.*

1 AUNT DAISY. Oh, you're back. Where've you been till this time?

2 JOBY. I went for a walk after Sunday School.

3 AUNT DAISY. Well, come on and get your tea, then we can wash up before we go to chapel.

She pours boiling water into a teapot, and follows JOBY *through.*

AUNT DAISY'S LIVING-ROOM

4 MONA. Who's preaching tonight, Mam?

5 AUNT DAISY. It's the Rev. Arthur Forrester. Not a preacher like Mr Featherstonhaugh, this morning—give a man a living and a dog-collar and it allus takes summat out of him. Still, he'll do. He's not a bad speaker.

They are all at table now.

6 JOBY. Did you see me mam, Auntie Daisy?

7 AUNT DAISY. Aye.

8 JOBY. How's she going on?

9 AUNT DAISY. She seemed nicely.

10 JOBY. Did she read me letter?

11 AUNT DAISY. Aye, and she sent you one back. [*Looks at* JOBY *accusingly.*] Why didn't you say you'd been up to the hospital last night? Why didn't you tell us when we asked you where you'd been?

12 JOBY. I don't know.

13 AUNT DAISY. You knew we'd get to know when you put it in that letter to your mam, didn't you?

14 JOBY. I don't know.

15 AUNT DAISY. What do you know? You know some sly, under-hand ways, don't you? Well, I'll tell you this: there's no room for 'em in *this* house.

16 JOBY. Can I have me mam's letter?

17 AUNT DAISY. Have you never learned to say please, neither?

45

1 JOBY. Please.

2 AUNT DAISY. That's more like it. Get him the letter out of me handbag, Mona. I don't know as he deserves it but I promised I'd give it to him.

MONA *gets the letter. He opens it and reads in silence.*

Aren't you going to tell us what she says, then?

3 JOBY [*reluctantly reads aloud*]. 'Dear Joby, Thank you for writing me a letter and telling me what you've been up to. After all your Auntie Daisy's done you could have told her as well. I'm very cross with you for coming up here when you know little boys are not allowed in and you are a very naughty boy for worrying your auntie after all she's done.

'So just mend your ways and show your auntie what a good lad you really are till I come home. I'm feeling quite well and I hope they'll tell me soon when I can come home. Love from Mam.'

4 AUNT DAISY. There, you see.

A series of swift scenes illustrating JOBY'S *deepening involvement with* GUS *and* TOMMY:

A PLAYING FIELD

The three of them are kicking an old football about.

A RAILWAY BRIDGE OVER THE RIVER

The three of them have crossed by traversing the outside of the girders. GUS *and* TOMMY, *ahead, jump down and wait for* JOBY. GUS *grins up at him.* JOBY *jumps down, relieved, and grins in return.*

AN ORCHARD

There is a shout from an unseen man as the three boys climb over the fence and, dropping under-ripe apples, flee at great speed across the adjoining field.

A SHOPPING STREET

JOBY *approaches a small chemist's shop with* GUS *and* TOMMY. *They go in.*

Joby hugs his mother, scared because she has to go into hospital for an operation, while his father carries on eating his breakfast

Aunt Daisy and her daughter, Mona, have come to take Joby to stay with them while his mother is in hospital

Gus tries to cause trouble while Joby and Snap wait for the beginning of the Saturday matinée

Joby confronted by a nursing sister while trying to slip into the hospital to see his mother

Gus and Tommy follow Joby into his house to share out the "loot"

Joby and Gus caught red-handed and forced by the shopkeeper to empty out their pockets

Norah Weston confronts her son with the evidence

Joby trying to persuade his father to return home

INSIDE THE CHEMIST'S SHOP

The CHEMIST *takes a prescription from* TOMMY.

1   CHEMIST. Is it for your father?

2   TOMMY. Yeh. He's had it before.

3   CHEMIST. It'll take a minute or two.

> TOMMY *nods and the* CHEMIST *goes into a room behind the shop. As soon as he has gone* GUS *and* TOMMY *begin to help themselves from the counter displays of barley sugar lozenges, diabetics' chocolate, herbal cigarettes.* JOBY *is for a moment rooted to the spot in astonished terror. Then he forces himself to open the door and step outside.*

OUTSIDE THE CHEMIST'S SHOP

> JOBY *comes out. He stands with his face to the window and looks to left and right. He forces himself to saunter unconcernedly away. He pauses a little way off and looks back at the shop.*
> A MAN *comes along and goes into the shop.* JOBY *looks round again, wondering whether to make his escape now, as he is sure to be implicated. Then the door opens and* GUS *and* TOMMY *come out,* GUS *carrying a medicine bottle wrapped in blue paper.* GUS *grins at* JOBY.

4   GUS. What did you buzz off out for?

5   JOBY. I thought you were gunna get copped any minute. Why didn't you tell me afore we went in?

6   GUS. Mebbe you wouldn't ha' come in with us if you'd known afore. Were you scared?

7   JOBY. Yeh, I was.

8   GUS. Oh, it's easy, man. [*Makes to move off.*] Anyway, we don't want to hang around here. You take that stuff home for your old feller, Tommy, and we'll find somewhere quiet to look what we've got.

OUTSIDE THE WESTONS' HOUSE

> GUS *waits at the back door.* JOBY *comes across the yard from the outside lavatory with the key in his hand.* TOMMY *runs round the corner as he opens the door. They go into the house.*

47

THE WESTONS' LIVING-ROOM

GUS *and* TOMMY *empty their loot on to the table.*

1 JOBY. Do you pinch from shops a lot?

2 GUS. We know one or two places, don't we Tommy?

3 TOMMY. Yeh, one or two.

   TOMMY *has a small bottle of scent.*

4 GUS. What you gunna do with that?

5 TOMMY. I dunno.

6 GUS. Why'd you pinch it, then?

7 TOMMY. I just picked it up.

8 GUS. You only wanna take stuff you can use.

9 TOMMY. Happen I'll chuck it away.

   He holds the bottle to the light, then opens it and smells at the contents.

   Pooh! Eau de kerniff.

10 GUS. Whyn't you give it to Joby, for his girl friend?

11 JOBY. What girl friend?

12 GUS. Elsa Laedeker. You're sweet on her, aren't you?

13 JOBY. Who's been spreading tales like that?

14 GUS. Oh, I dunno. I just thought you were sweet on her,
   that's all.

15 JOBY. I've never even talked to her.

16 GUS. You wanna give her a present, man. A little bottle o'
   scent, or summat like that.

17 JOBY. How can I when I don't talk to her?

18 GUS. Aw, you can allus manage to talk to her if you want to.

   TOMMY *holds the bottle out to* JOBY.

19 TOMMY. Want it, then?

20 JOBY [*hesitates*]. Might as well, if you don't want it.

   He takes it. There is a knock on the door.

21 GUS. Who's that?

22 JOBY. I dunno.

48

1   GUS. Wait a jiffy.

    He and TOMMY *sweep up the stuff and hide it. The knock sounds again.* JOBY *goes through into the hall.*

    OUTSIDE THE WESTONS' HOUSE

    SNAP *is on the step as* JOBY *opens the door.* JOBY *steps out and pulls the door to behind him.*

2   JOBY. Oh, hello, Snap.

3   SNAP. Hi, Joby. How you doing?

4   JOBY. Oh, okay.

5   SNAP. Are you coming out?

6   JOBY. No, I can't now.

7   SNAP. What about tomorrow?

8   JOBY. I've fixed up to go with Gus and Tommy.

9   SNAP. Where to?

10 JOBY. I dunno yet.

11 SNAP. Are you knocking about with them now?

12 JOBY. Yeh, I have been a bit. [*pause.*] I heard about your uncle.

13 SNAP. Yeh.

    Pause.

14 JOBY. I reckon it'll be okay if you want to come with us.

15 SNAP. Naw, I don't like Gus Wilson.

16 JOBY. He's okay when you get to know him.

17 SNAP. Well, he doesn't like me, anyway.

    Pause.

18 JOBY. I shall have to go back in now.

19 SNAP. Has your mam come home yet?

20 JOBY. No, not yet.

21 SNAP. I'll see you some other time, then.

    He begins to mooch off.

22 JOBY. Yeh, see you, Snap!

    He stands and looks after SNAP *for a moment before going back into the house.*

THE WESTONS' LIVING-ROOM

JOBY *comes back in.*

1   JOBY. It was only Snap.

2   GUS. Oh, him. Is he off, now?

3   JOBY. Yeh, he's gone.

They get the loot out again. GUS *opens a packet of herbal cigarettes and lights one.*

4   GUS. Ugh! Herbal. Rammy. Want one, Joby?

5   JOBY. No.

6   GUS. Have a cough spice, then.

7   JOBY. I'll have one of them barley sugars.

GUS *tosses a packet across.*

8   GUS. Here, help yourself. [*He leans back in his chair and puffs at the cigarette.*] Mmmm. I reckon you could get used to 'em. Anyway they didn't cost owt, did they?

The droll way GUS *delivers this breaks them up. They laugh till they are almost weeping.*

SHOPPING STREET

JOBY *watches as* ELSA LAEDEKER *and her* FATHER *come out of a bank and get into their car. They drive away.* JOBY *turns homewards.*

OUTSIDE THE WESTONS' HOUSE

JOBY *comes out of the lavatory, having failed to find the house key. He looks puzzled as he crosses the yard to the door. He tries the door and finds it open. He goes into the house.*

THE WESTONS' LIVING-ROOM

JOBY *enters and calls out.*

9   JOBY. Anybody in?

He thinks he hears a sound from upstairs. He goes into the hall and calls up.

Dad? Mona?

JOBY starts to climb the stairs. He is halfway up when a figure jumps out of his bedroom, wearing a gas mask and uttering a terrible cry. JOBY turns and retreats. GUS pulls off the mask and collapses with laughter on the stairs.

1   JOBY. You scared me out of me flippin' wits. What you doing in here on your own?

     GUS *comes down.*

2   GUS. Waiting for you. I thought you were going to mess your pants, man.

     They go into the living-room.

3   JOBY. How'd you get in?

4   GUS. I saw where you kept your key.

5   JOBY. You shouldn't be in here on your own.

6   GUS. Aw, don't be like that. We're mates, aren't we?

7   JOBY. Where's Tommy?

8   GUS. He's gone on his holidays. Everybody's gone. There's nobody about at all.

9   JOBY. We'd ha' been going, only me mam was waiting to go into hospital.

10   GUS. Ey, I've had an idea. I know a lass called Joan Birch what goes to play with Elsa Laedeker at their house.

11   JOBY. What about it, then?

12   GUS. Well, you can send a letter to her, man, and that scent 'at Tommy gave you. Then you might get talking to her.

13   JOBY. You mean if I write a letter you'll give it to this Joan Birch?

14   GUS. Yeh.

15   JOBY. What if she goes blabbin' it all over the place?

16   GUS. Aw, she won't do that. You leave it to me. [JOBY *hesitates.*] Go on, man. What you waiting for?

17   JOBY. I'm thinking about it.

A QUIET BACK STREET

JOBY and GUS walk along, throwing an old tennis ball diagonally to each other across the width of the street. A MAN laboriously pedalling

a 'stop me and buy one' ice-cream tricycle comes round the corner.
JOBY *throws the ball higher and* GUS *misses it.* GUS *retrieves it as it*
bounces near the front of a little general shop. JOBY *crosses over to him*
as he looks into the window. GUS *turns and grins at* JOBY.

1 GUS. Got any gelt?

   JOBY *feels in his pocket.*

2 JOBY. Threepence ha'penny. Haven't you got owt?

3 GUS. Not a cent. What can we ask for that isn't much?

4 JOBY. Chewing gum.

5 GUS. Aye, that's it.

6 JOBY. Have you been in this one before?

7 GUS. No, but it'll be okay. Want me to ask?

8 JOBY. Yeh, you ask.

   He hands GUS *a penny and* GUS *leads the way into the shop.*

   GENERAL SHOP

   An old fashioned general grocer's. They enter and wait. Nobody
   appears. GUS *dips his hand into an open box of toffees.* JOBY *goes for*
   another box. GUS *reaches right over the counter to the cigarettes. But*
   the GROCER *has come through a door behind them. He quietly moves*
   between them and the outer door. He suddenly speaks, petrifying them.

9 GROCER. And what d'you think you're doing? [*He throws the*
   bolt on the door.] I asked you what you thought you were
   doing.

10 GUS. We wanted some chewing gum, please.

11 JOBY [*babbles*]. Yes, that's right. Just some chewing gum. He's
   got the money for it.

   GUS *opens hand and shows money.*

12 GROCER. Chewing gum, eh? Well, you won't find it in the
   box o' toffees, nor under the counter. Come over here.
   [*He walks behind the counter.*] Now empty your pockets.

13 JOBY. You're not going to fetch a bobby, are you, mister?

14 GROCER. Is that all? [*He looks at what they have taken from their pockets,*
   including the envelope containing the letter to ELSA, *and the scent. He*
   picks that up.] What's this?

1   GUS. A letter I'm posting for me mam.

2   GROCER. There's no name and address on it.

3   GUS. No, she hadn't time to write it on, so I'm taking it
    straight round to me auntie's.

4   GROCER. What's your name? Your real one, mind.

5   GUS. John Wilson.

6   GROCER. And who might you be?

7   JOBY. Joseph Weston. Everybody calls me Joby.

8   GROCER. What would you think to everybody calling you
    'thief'?

9   JOBY [*mumbles*]. I wouldn't like it.

10 GROCER. No . . . Well, you'd better tell me what made you
    come into my shop to steal. How long have you been
    doing this kind o'thing? Do you do it in every shop you
    go into?

11 GUS. No, we're not thieves, Mister, honest. We just thought
    it'd be a bit o' fun. It was a sort o' dare, like, you know.
    We were a bit fed-up, with all our mates off on their
    holidays an' that. We'd never do it again, would we,
    Joby?

12 GROCER. Fun, eh? You know where that kind o' fun'll land
    you, don't you? Into reform school. And there's no
    home comforts there, nor holidays at the seaside, either.
    And when you get out everybody'll know you for
    convicted thieves and nobody'll trust you any more.
    What sort of a start in life is that? What school do you go
    to?

13 GUS. Tinsley Road.

14 JOBY. I'm going to Cressley Grammar School in September.

15 GROCER [*in a tone of weary exasperation*]. Then why the hangman
    do you want to spoil such a chance by carrying on like
    this? [*He goes to the door and unlocks it.*] Pick up your stuff and
    get off home. And have a good think about what I've
    told you.

    Theyy eagerl scrape up their belongings.

16 GUS. Are you going to tell us dads?

1   GROCER. You'd better wait and see about that. But remember this—I know who you are and if I hear tell about you getting into any more scrapes like this Is'll go straight to the police and tell 'em about today.

2   GUS. Don't worry, Mister. We shan't get into any more trouble.

The GROCER *opens the door.*

3   GROCER. Get off home. Just think on what I've told you an' you'll be all right.

4   JOBY. Thanks, Mister. Thanks very much.

OUTSIDE THE SHOP

JOBY *and* GUS *leave the shop. They walk along together in silence until they reach the seclusion of an alley.*

5   GUS. Crikey! I thought we were in for it that time.

6   JOBY. Me an' all. I reckon we'd better stop it now.

7   GUS. Aye, it's not safe any more.

A church clock strikes the half hour.

8   JOBY. What time's that, then?

9   GUS. Half past four.

10   JOBY. Is'll have to be off to me auntie's for me tea.

11   GUS. Aw, there's plenty of time. [*He looks round to see if anyone is coming.*] What about having a quick drag first?

He takes a new ten-packet of Woodbines out of his pocket.

12   JOBY. Where'd you get *them*?

13   GUS [*grins*]. Where'd you think?

14   JOBY. But you gave 'em all back.

15   GUS. All except these.

JOBY *is forced to grin in reluctant admiration, though all he can really think of now is getting away from* GUS.

16   JOBY. Honest, Gus, you're the blinkin' limit.

17   GUS. Well, are we gunna light up?

1　JOBY. No. Me auntie carries on summat wild if I'm late. I'll see you later. So long.

He walks away, breaking into a trot and, before he turns a corner, looks back to see GUS *still in the alley, a little cloud of smoke coming up off his cigarette.*

OUTSIDE THE WESTONS' HOUSE

A big black taxi draws up outside the house as JOBY *turns the corner.* JOBY'S MOTHER *and* FATHER *get out.* JOBY'S MOTHER *stands and looks at the house and about while* WESTON *pays the driver. Then they go into the house together.* JOBY'S *delight gives way to apprehension as he thinks of his recent escapades.*

Part Four

THE WESTONS' LIVING-ROOM

JOBY *sits quietly on one side, reading a comic, while his* MOTHER *listens to their neighbour,* MRS COLLINS, *who has come to borrow a cup of sugar and stopped to gossip.*

1 MRS COLLINS. An' then—you'll never credit it—he came to right in the middle of his operation and there was all his stomach laid out on the table at the side of him. They'd never put him out properly, y'see.

2 NORAH. Heavens above! Whatever happened then?

3 MRS COLLINS. Well, he just laid there ever so quiet for a minute, watching what they were doing like. An' then one of 'em spotted he wa' wide awake an' give him another whiff of the ether, right sharp.

4 NORAH. I should just think so.

5 MRS COLLINS. O' course, Frank had a professional interest in it like, him having been a first-aid man all his married life; and he said afterwards he wished they'd left him alone so's he could watch a bit longer. He said they didn't half make a fuss of him after, trying to pass it over, y'see, so's he wouldn't lodge any complaints, him knowing the ropes and all that. [*Pause.*] There's a lot goes on in them places at nobody outside ever gets to know about, y'know. When all's said and done, you put your life in their hands an' if they make a mistake they all stick up for one another. Thick as thieves, they are, in hospitals.

6 NORAH. I must say they did well enough for me, in the General.

7 MRS COLLINS. Ah, but that wasn't as bad as you thought, was it? It's when you get complications 'at trouble starts. Like when I had our Walter. [*Sits.*] By, but he caused some trouble getting here, that lad. Blood? You've never seen so much. That delivery room wa' just like a slaughter-house. For all the world as if they'd been killing a beast.

1 NORAH. Aren't you going out to play, Joby?

2 JOBY. In a minute. I'm just finishing me comic.

3 MRS COLLINS. Aye, what a do that was. An' then when I had
   our Margaret it was as different again. As easy as shelling
   peas. And that reminds me—have you heard about that
   Macleod lass up the street?

4 NORAH. No, what about her?

   JOBY *pricks his ears up now.*

5 MRS COLLINS. They say she's having a bairn . . .

6 NORAH. Joby, off you go out and play, while the sun's still
   shining.

   JOBY *gets up, only too glad to go now.*

7 MRS COLLINS. It's all up and down the street. I allus knew
   she'd get herself into a mess afore she'd done.

   JOBY *goes out.*

   RUNCIBLE STREET

   In the grip of yet another alarm, JOBY *emerges into the street. A
   football rolls towards him from a group of bigger lads playing up the
   street. One of them shouts to him.*

8 BIG LAD. Ey, young 'un! [JOBY *looks up.*] Kick us that ball.

   JOBY *kicks the ball back to them and wanders off along the street.
   Kerb-crawling towards him, with the* DRIVER *apparently trying to
   make out the house numbers, is a motor car which* JOBY *finds vaguely
   familiar, but it is not until it stops alongside him and the* DRIVER
   speaks to him with a faint foreign accent that JOBY *realizes whom he
   must be.*

9 MR LAEDEKER. Young man, can you tell me where the
   Westons live, please?

10 JOBY. Number twenty-nine. This side.

11 MR LAEDEKER. Thank you very much.

   JOBY *walks away before the man can ask him anything else. He stops at
   the corner and watches him get out of the car and knock on the front
   door. Then* JOBY *breaks into a run.*

OUTSIDE SNAP'S HOUSE

JOBY *approaches the house and knocks. There is no answer. He knocks again. A frail* OLD LADY *in a shawl comes to the door of the next house.*

1 OLD LADY. It's no use knocking there, young man. They've all gone on their holidays, to Bridlington.

2 JOBY. Have they gone for the week?

3 OLD LADY. As far as I know. Was it young Sidney you wanted?

4 JOBY. Yes.

5 OLD LADY. Well, they all gone, so you'll have to wait till they come back.

6 JOBY. Righto.

He walks away, disappointed.

RUNCIBLE STREET

JOBY *comes round the corner and looks along the street.* MR LAEDEKER'S *car has gone. He wanders slowly towards home, wondering what he will have to face there.* MOLLIE MACLEOD *comes hurtling out of an entry and almost cannons into* JOBY.

7 MOLLIE. Ey, Joby, what you doing?

8 JOBY. Just going in home.

9 MOLLIE. Ey, have you heard? Looks as if there'll be no more tanners out of our lass.

10 JOBY. Why, what's up?

11 MOLLIE. There's nowt to tell on her about now. [*Gleeful.*] Haven't you heard? The big daft devil's got herself into trouble. She's having a kid.

12 JOBY. You mean your Agnes?

13 MOLLIE. Hadn't you heard?

14 JOBY. Well, I did hear summat . . .

15 MOLLIE. It's our lass. [*Pause.*] You didn't think it was me, did you? [*Laughs.*] You an' me couldn't make a kid. Anyway, we didn't do anything to make one.

16 JOBY. You don't have to tell me. I'm not daft.

He turns and walks away from MOLLIE. *She calls after him.*

1   MOLLIE. You ask your mam to tell you all about it.

THE WESTONS' LIVING-ROOM

JOBY'S MOTHER *is alone. The little phial of perfume stands in the centre of the tablecloth.* JOBY *enters.*

2   NORAH. Come in, you. I want to talk to you.

3   JOBY. What about?

4   NORAH [*points*]. Have you seen that before?

5   JOBY. What is it?

6   NORAH. What is it? You can see what it is. I want to know if you've seen it before.

7   JOBY. I might have.

8   NORAH. Oh, you might have. And how might you have?

9   JOBY. I don't know what you mean.

10 NORAH. Well, happen this'll make it plainer. [*She takes a folded piece of notepaper from her apron pocket, opens it and lays it on the table.*] Is that your writing? [JOBY *nods.*] Love letters to lasses, at your age.

11 JOBY. It's not a love letter.

12 NORAH. We won't argue about that. What I'm bothered about is that bottle o'scent.

13 JOBY. Have you had somebody to see you?

14 NORAH. Yes, I've had Mr Laedeker. He's a very nice man. When his daughter receives expensive presents from strange boys he likes to know what it's all about.

15 JOBY. It wasn't expensive.

16 NORAH. How much was it, then?

JOBY *hesitates for a fraction of a second.*

17 JOBY. Half a crown.

18 NORAH. Not quick enough, lad. And not true, either. Mr Laedeker took the trouble to find out about it, and he says a bottle of perfume like that costs eleven and sixpence in a chemist's shop. Now, where did you get eleven and sixpence from to buy it?

19 JOBY. I didn't buy it. I had it given.

1   NORAH. That's a likely story. Now, I'm warning you, young man, I'm in the mood to give you a good hiding, so you'd better make up your mind to tell me the truth.

2   JOBY. It is the truth. Another lad gave it to me.

3   NORAH. Who was he?

4   JOBY. I can't tell.

5   NORAH. You mean, you won't. How do you expect me to believe you if you won't tell me who he is?

6   JOBY. I can't split on him, Mam.

7   NORAH. Did this lad steal the scent?

8   JOBY. Yeh, I think so.

9   NORAH. And yet you took it, knowing it to be stolen. Now, Joby, look me in the face and tell me the truth. Did you steal it yourself?

10   JOBY. I didn't pinch it.

11   NORAH. Was it that mate of yours—Snap?

12   JOBY. No, Snap's not like that.

13   NORAH. Well, that's one point in his favour, anyway. I never knew you were like that before. I don't know what you've been up to while I've been away . . . You deserve a damn' good hiding and if your father wasn't away visiting your Uncle Clifford, in Rochdale, he'd give you one. Get off to bed.

14   JOBY. But it's only half past three!

15   NORAH. You're going upstairs, all the same. Happen you'll have time to think what sort of a lad you've turned into. And p'raps you'll think of a few more things you ought to tell me.

She turns away.

16   JOBY [*after a pause*]. I'm sorry, Mam.

17   NORAH. And so you should be. Now get off up and get undressed.

18   JOBY. Can I read for a bit?

19   NORAH. Oh, I reckon so. If you go to sleep now you'll never sleep tonight.

JOBY goes out and slowly mounts the stairs.

JOBY'S BEDROOM

JOBY *enters and undresses. He finds one of his favourite books,
'Coral Island', and gets into bed with it. In a moment he turns on his
side and snuggles down, still reading.*

THE SAME   Evening

JOBY *is asleep, the book lying open. He wakes as he hears voices from
the living-room below. He gets out of bed, goes to the door and opens it.
He goes out.*

STAIRS AND HALLWAY

JOBY *comes quietly downstairs and stands outside the living-room
door. His* MOTHER, AUNT DAISY *and* MONA *are in there talking,
their voices charged with feeling.*

THE WESTONS' LIVING-ROOM

A fading evening light.

1 NORAH. It's all very well for you to drag our Mona round
   here by the scruff of the neck. What do you expect me to
   say, Daisy, until I hear Reg's side of it? I reckon he'll have
   summat to say when he comes home.

2 AUNT DAISY. *If* he comes home. If you ask me he'll be too
   ashamed to show his face round here for a bit. Anyway,
   you sound as if you don't believe what our Mona says.

3 NORAH. You know how she is. She's bloody gormless enough
   to imagine owt.

4 MONA [*wails*]. Oh, Auntie Norah!

5 NORAH. It's no good you Oh, Auntie Norah-ing me now.
   You should have sense enough to know not to mess
   about with married men, wheedling round 'em till they
   don't know whether they're coming or going!

6 AUNT DAISY. Now just a minute, Norah. I'm not having that.
   Our Mona's a straightforward lass, for all her faults.
   She's never had any trouble with men before. You're
   not trying to tell me it was her idea to run off like that.

7 NORAH. Happen not. But she wants a damn' good clout to
   brighten her ideas up.

1   AUNT DAISY. And she's had one. She got one when she come home and told me what had happened. And she'll likely get another when Ted hears about it.

2   MONA. Oh, I'm sorry, Mam, I'm sorry. I wish it had never happened.

3   AUNT DAISY. You should ha' thought about that afore, instead o'bringing disgrace on us all. You know I'll never be able to hold me head up in t'street again. How do you think *I* feel about it, eh? But I'm only your mother.

4   NORAH. Happen you'll feel better if you don't blab it all over the place and try to make a martyr of yourself.

5   AUNT DAISY. Why, Norah. I don't know how you can say such things.

6   NORAH. I know you, Daisy. You're allus looking for slights where there aren't any and setting yourself up as a flamin' whited sepulchre.

7   AUNT DAISY. I've done nowt but try to live a clean an' upright life an' do my duty as I see it. An' the world 'ud be a sight better place if everybody else did the same.

8   NORAH. It'd be a sorrier place for you, with nobody to look down on.

9   AUNT DAISY. Oh, Norah!

10   NORAH. I know you're upset but you can't tell me there isn't a bit of you enjoying it.

11   AUNT DAISY. Why, I've never heard such talk in my life. I don't know how you can. . .

     JOBY *opens the door and walks into the room.*

12   NORAH. And what are you doing out of bed, young man?

13   JOBY. I want some supper.

14   NORAH. Well there is none.

15   JOBY. Can I have a drink of water, then?

     NORAH *runs a tumbler of water for him and gives him two plain biscuits.*

16   NORAH. Here, take these with you and don't make crumbs all over the bedclothes.

1 JOBY. Has me Dad come home yet?

2 NORAH. No. He'll happen be back in the morning.

AUNT DAISY *snorts and* JOBY *sees his* MOTHER'S *mouth tighten.*

Go on, off you go back to bed.

3 JOBY. I'm not tired now.

4 NORAH. It makes no difference. Go on, get off.

JOBY *goes out.* NORAH *closes door behind him.*

5 AUNT DAISY. That poor bairn.

6 NORAH. Oh, don't talk so soft, Daisy.

NORAH *opens door to hall and goes quickly through.* JOBY *has gone halfway up the stairs but is now creeping down again.*

7 NORAH. Joby, did you hear me? I shan't tell you again.

JOBY *hastily retreats up the stairs as* NORAH *returns to the living-room.*

8 AUNT DAISY. You're a hard woman, Norah.

9 NORAH. Me? Hard? I allus thought you were the hard one in the family, Daisy.

10 AUNT DAISY. You must ha' been hard with Reg an' all, or he'd not have done what he has. Men don't do that sort o' thing without reason.

11 NORAH. Oh, so I'm to blame for it now, am I?

12 AUNT DAISY. You must have given him cause, Norah.

13 NORAH. Cause? There's your cause, sitting there with her big bust and her bare legs.

14 AUNT DAISY. You can't have been to him what you should have been.

15 NORAH. A damn' fine chance I've had this past few months, haven't I? And when I've gone through all that and come out of hospital, what do I find? That me own niece has been making up to me husband while I was out of the way. Well it's a pity she didn't do it with some single young feller who'd get her in a field and show her what's what.

1 AUNT DAISY. You can't be sure your Reg hasn't shown her, can you?

2 MONA. Oh, Mam, I told you—

3 NORAH. Well, we'd better get to know, then, while we're about it.

4 AUNT DAISY. She says he hasn't hardly touched her.

5 NORAH. I'd like to hear for meself. Come on, Mona, out with it.

6 MONA. I've told me mam. He only kissed me. I wouldn't let him do anything else.

7 NORAH. Did he try?

8 MONA. He touched . . . he touched me here, once or twice.

   Hand to her breast.

9 AUNT DAISY. Did he put his hand inside your clothes?

10 MONA. No, I wouldn't let him. He wanted me to. He said I were driving him mad. He said he loved me. I told him not to be so daft, but he kept on trying. He said we could go to Blackpool for a bit and have a holiday and then he'd find another job and get a divorce so's we could get married.

11 NORAH. My God!

   JOBY *is outside again, listening.*

12 AUNT DAISY. Aye, you need say so, Norah. You need say so. That's right, go on, you shed a few tears. I was wondering when you were going to.

13 MONA. And when we got to Manchester I got frightened, so I run off the train and let it go without me.

14 NORAH. To think he had to make a fool of himself over a big soft lump like you.

15 AUNT DAISY. If you're going to get nasty, Norah, we'd better go.

16 NORAH. Aye, you better had. You're doing no good here.

17 AUNT DAISY. Don't think you've heard the last of it, though.

18 NORAH. Are you daft, Daisy? My husband's God knows where, and you talk about not hearing the last of it.

1 AUNT DAISY. We'll leave you to think about it. You might try offering up a word of prayer.

2 NORAH. Oh, get off, and take your flamin' humbug with you.

3 AUNT DAISY. I'm warning you, Norah. I've done me best to be fair and patient, but you're trying me too far.

4 NORAH. Good night, Daisy.

5 AUNT DAISY. I'll be round in the morning.

6 NORAH. You've no need.

As AUNT DAISY *ushers* MONA *out before her,* JOBY *goes quickly up the stairs.*

7 AUNT DAISY. Ah, but I want a few words with Master Reg. *If he comes back.*

AUNT DAISY *and* MONA *walk along hall and out through front door.*

JOBY'S BEDROOM

Light fading into dusk. JOBY *sits on the edge of his bed and drinks deeply from the glass and bites into one of the biscuits. There is no sound from below. He finds and puts on his socks and goes out on to the landing.*

THE WESTONS' HALLWAY

JOBY *comes slowly down the dark stairs. He hesitates outside the living-room door, then opens it and goes in.*

THE WESTONS' LIVING-ROOM

Almost dark now. JOBY *opens the door hesitantly, then comes slowly in. He can make out his* MOTHER *sitting quietly in the shadows.*

8 JOBY. Don't you want a light on?

9 NORAH. No. I don't want to look at anything.

10 JOBY. Hasn't me dad come back yet?

11 NORAH. No, not yet.

12 JOBY. When will he come back?

13 NORAH. Tomorrow, happen. [*Pause.*] You'd better go back to bed.

14 JOBY. Aren't you coming?

1   NORAH. In a bit.

    Pause.

2   JOBY. Mam . . .

3   NORAH. What?

4   JOBY. I'm sorry, Mam. I mean about the scent and all that.

    *She says nothing and in a moment he goes back to the door. He has the
    impression she is crying but he can't see her face in the dusk and she
    makes no sound.* JOBY *turns slowly to go back up to bed.*

    THE WESTONS' LIVING-ROOM   Next evening

    NORAH *is ironing clothes.* JOBY *sits at the table with an open comic in
    front of him. It is Sunday. He is wearing his best suit and new shoes.*

5   JOBY. An' if I had a bike to go on we'd save it on bus fares in
    no time.

6   NORAH. We'll have to wait an' see.

7   JOBY. It doesn't have to be a new 'un.

8   NORAH. It's them roads down in Cressley. They're very busy.

9   JOBY. I'll have to learn sometime, Mam.

10 NORAH. Well, just let it drop for now.

11 JOBY [*after a pause*]. Is me Uncle Clifford right poorly?

12 NORAH. I only know what your dad told me. He got the
    telephone call at work.

13 JOBY. Can't we telephone me Auntie Alice and find out when
    me dad's coming home?

14 NORAH [*wearily*]. Joby, will you stop pestering and either read
    your comic quietly or go out?

    A knock at the street door

15 AUNT DAISY. Anybody in?

    She comes in, followed by her husband, JOBY'S UNCLE TED.

16 NORAH. Hello, Daisy.

17 AUNT DAISY. Norah.

18 NORAH. Oh, you're here are you, Ted?

    UNCLE TED *is ill at ease and does not know where to look.*

66

1   TED. It's a bit of a mess, taken all round, isn't it?

2   NORAH. Aye.

3   TED. You've had no word yet, then?

4   NORAH. No.

5   TED. You don't think you happen ought to inform t'police?

6   NORAH. What for? It's no business of theirs. He's free to go as
    he pleases, and come back t'same way.

7   AUNT DAISY. You can't just sit back and take that attitude,
    Norah.

8   NORAH. I can take whatever attitude I like. Joby, off you go
    out and play.

    JOBY *makes no argument, but gets up and leaves the house.*

    RAILWAY BRIDGE, MEADOW, RIVERBANK, ENVIRONS

    JOBY *is walking in a large circuit of a rural edge of the township until*
    AUNT DAISY *and* UNCLE TED *will have gone and it will be time for
    bed. He comes down some steps on to a railway bridge. He is wearing
    new shoes with his usual neat Sunday clothes and they are beginning to
    rub his heel. He stops and tries to ease them by pushing in his finger.
    He goes on, passing* A COUPLE *taking their Sunday evening constitu-
    tional. He goes along a path or lane and comes into a meadow. By
    now the shoes are really uncomfortable and he stops and takes one off
    and pulls down his sock and examines his heel. He puts the shoe back
    on and continues. When he comes in sight of the river he sees, some
    way off, the figure of a man sitting alone, on the bank. He walks a
    little closer and stops as he recognizes his* FATHER. *At first he feels an
    impulse to hide. Then he goes towards him, stopping some yards away
    as he speaks first.*

9   JOBY. Hello, Dad.

    WESTON *is wearing his best suit and a new cap. He comes dully out of
    his reverie and looks round.*

10 WESTON. Hello, Joby.

11 JOBY. What you doing here, Dad?

12 WESTON. Oh, just sitting and thinking.

13 JOBY. What you thinking about?

1   WESTON. Things you wouldn't understand.

    JOBY goes a little nearer.

2   JOBY. They're all up at home, wondering where you are.

3   WESTON. Who's there?

4   JOBY. Me mam, an' Auntie Daisy—and Uncle Ted an' all. Happen they'll have gone now.

5   WESTON. What had they to say?

6   JOBY. I didn't hear much. Me Uncle Ted was asking me mam if she wanted to fetch the police. [*Pause as* WESTON *does not respond.*] Me mam said she wouldn't, though. They sent me out then. Do they want the bobby to look for you, Dad?

7   WESTON. I expect so.

    JOBY sits down a little way from his FATHER *and looks at the black surface of the river.*

8   JOBY. I wish we had a nice clean river, like they have at Ilkley, then happen we could get some fish in it. [*Pause.*] Me Auntie Daisy an' our Mona were round last night, late on. Our Mona was crying and me auntie said she'd been clouting her. She sounded mad and me mam stood up to her and told her where she got off. I was supposed to be in bed but I went down for a drink and listened through the door. Me mam didn't cry then but I think she did when they'd gone. I couldn't really see 'cos she was sitting in the dark and she wouldn't let me put the light on. [*Pause.*] Have you been away somewhere with our Mona?

9   WESTON. You wouldn't understand, Joby. You're too young.

10 JOBY [*after a pause*]. You like our Mona, don't you? I knew you did when I saw you cuddling her in me Auntie Daisy's scullery. I've never seen you cuddling me mam.

11 WESTON. You don't see everything. You see too much as it is.

    A long pause.

12 JOBY. D'you like our Mona better than me mam? Did you go away so's you could be with her?

His FATHER *puts his face down on his knees and groans.*

1   WESTON. I've done summat I'll never live down. [*A silence. He lifts his head.*] Why don't you hoppit and leave me alone? What you want to come down here for in t'first place?

2   JOBY. I was just wandering about. They made me go out so's they could talk, and I didn't know where to go so I came down here.

3   WESTON. You should be home in bed, out of it all.

4   JOBY. It's getting dark. Me mam'll be wondering where we are.

5   WESTON. She'll be wondering where *you* are. You'd better be getting off home.

6   JOBY. D'you want me to tell her I've seen you?

7   WESTON. I reckon you won't be able to help yourself.

    JOBY *reluctantly stands up.*

8   JOBY. Aren't you coming?

9   WESTON. Not just yet. I'll sit here a while longer.

10 JOBY. Have I to tell her you're coming?

11 WESTON. Tell her what you like. Go on, get off. It's turning chilly and you've nowt much on you. You'll catch cold.

    JOBY *walks away from him up a little slope and to a gap in a hedge. He looks back at his* FATHER *sitting hugging his knees in the gathering darkness. He goes through the gap and starts across the field. He is limping now and he stops and sits down and eases off the shoe, gingerly feeling at his heel. He puts the shoe back on and stands up. Then he looks back the way he has come. Suddenly panic hits him. He goes in a stumbling run back the way he came until he reaches the gap in the hedge. From there he can see the river bank. But there is now no sign of his* FATHER, *only the flattened patch of grass where he was sitting.* JOBY *goes down on to the bank and looks both ways. Then he goes as near the edge of the bank as he dare and looks at the greasy sliding water.*

12 JOBY [*softly, terrified*]. What can I do? Oh, what can I do? [*He lifts his head and shouts.*] Dad! Dad! Where are you? [*He senses rather than sees a movement behind a clump of bushes a second before* WESTON *steps into view, fastening his flies.* JOBY *hurls himself*

69

at him and clutches him round the waist.] Dad! Oh Dad, I was
scared. I came back to look for you and you weren't
there.

2 WESTON. I thought I told you to go home?

3 JOBY. I couldn't go without you. I was scared of leaving you
down here by yourself. Oh, come on home with me,
Dad. It'll be all right. Me mam's waiting for you. You
don't care about me Auntie Daisy an' them, do you?
They don't matter to us, do they?

4 WESTON. No, I don't reckon they do, when it comes right
down to it. [*He pushes* JOBY *gently away from him.*] Come on,
then, stop your roarin'. You don't want your mam to
see you like that. [*He gives* JOBY *his handkerchief.*] Here use
that. [*They begin to walk together towards the gap in the hedge and*
WESTON *notices* JOBY's *difficulty in walking.*] Is there summat
wrong with your foot?

5 JOBY. Me shoe's rubbing it. It's ever so sore.

6 WESTON. Think you can manage to walk home?

7 JOBY. I don't think I can. I think it'll start bleeding in a
minute.

8 WESTON. Hold on. [*He squats down in the path.*] Get up on me
shoulders and I'll see if I can carry you.

JOBY *gets up with his thighs on each side of* WESTON's *neck and*
WESTON *rises to his full height and begins to walk in long, easy*
strides

All right?

9 JOBY. All right if you are.

10 WESTON. Is'll manage. You've got to be a bit heavier since I
last carried you like this.

JOBY *gets the hang of balancing and swaying to the motion of his*
FATHER's *strides. He senses his* FATHER *relapsing into thought and*
curbs his own desire to chatter. He rides in silence, looking about him
at the approaching night. He is eight feet tall and from where he rides
he can see the lights of the town sprinkled across the dark hillside.
Somewhere among them is the light of home. He can't see it, but he
knows it is there.

THE END

70

Notes and Questions

TWO EXTRACTS FROM THE NOVEL, 'JOBY'

In the first extract (which corresponds to a scene in Part Two of the television play) Joby goes to the children's Saturday film show.

'Where you been?' Snap said. 'I thought you weren't coming.'

'Aw, it was me Auntie Daisy,' Joby said. It was enough, without enlarging. 'Anyway, we're not late.'

'No, but there'll be a bigger queue.'

'Ne'er mind.'

There was a queue, one of the biggest they had seen for a tuppenny rush, stretching nearly a hundred yards along the pavement from the cinema.

'Think we'll get in?' Snap said.

' 'Course,' Joby said. 'Have you got enough gelt to go upstairs?'

'Aye, but I shan't be able to get any spice.'

Though it was called the tuppenny rush, it was only the hard seats in the first six rows of stalls that were tuppence on Saturday afternoon. The rest of the seats downstairs were threepence, and in the circle it was fourpence a time. Joby liked going upstairs; it was a bit quieter and even if the kids in front of you bounced about, as they often did when the picture became exciting, you could still see because the seats were steeply raked.

Joby told Snap to keep their places while he went and got some sweets. He queued in the little shop across the street and bought a bar of treacle toffee and twopenn'orth of old-fashioned humbugs—the big buttery kind—and came out as the cinema doors were opened and the line of young people began to move forward.

The cinema was perhaps doing particularly good business this afternoon because they were showing the last episode of their current serial and everybody was eager to know how Flash Gordon would finally deal with that nasty old Ming the Merciless. Perhaps Ming would fall into a bottomless pit of smoke and flames (there were several about) or be struck down by a ray gun. Joby thought it would be a good wheeze to let him get half way across a light-bridge then switch the current off and send him to his death between the high buildings. Or maybe they would put the electrodes to his temples and turn him into a robot as he had done to the professor early in the serial. Then there were the claymen, slaves of Ming, who materialized out of the walls of the subterranean passages under Ming's palace. Something had to be done to bring them back to normal.

Joby and Snap discussed the possibilities as they moved towards the pay-box, as well as speculating on the feature film—a Buck Jones—and the new serial. For the crafty management, intent upon keeping interest at a peak, were following the last episode of 'Flash Gordon' with the first of 'Jungle Jim'.

Gus Wilson and some of his mates were sitting in the row behind Joby and Snap. There were a couple of girls next to them and Gus kept leaning over and pretending to pass on remarks that Tommy Masterman had made about one of them.

'Ey, he says you've got gorgeous eyes.'

'Gerraway with you,' the lass said.

'He says they're like pools,' Gus said, killing himself: 'football pools.'

'I'm taking no notice,' the lass said.

Tommy was wriggling about with embarrassment.

'Lay off, Gus, will you.'

'Well, you said you liked her, didn't you?'

'I never. When did I say that?'

'Ah, go on, you know you said it.'

'I never did. Me say I liked her!'

Joby took another look and saw that the girl was Snotty Marlowe, from Foundry Yard; a thin ugly girl who had a perpetually running nose which she hardly ever bothered to wipe clean.

'Ey, he says will you swap places with me so's he can sit next to you.'

'Tell him to go run up a shutter,' Snotty said.

'He says he'll buy you an ice cream at the interval if you do.'

'She'll have to flippin' well pay for it herself,' Tommy said. 'I've no brass.'

Gus laughed.

'Ey, look who's here. It's Copperknob. You'd better keep that ginger nut down when the picture's on, kid.'

'You can see, can't you?' Snap said.

'If I can't I'll bray your head down into your shoulders,' Gus said; 'like this.'

He clenched his fists, put the left one on top of Snap's head and beat on it with his right.

Snap squirmed out of the way.

'Why can't you leave people alone, Gus Wilson?'

'What d'you mean by that?'

'You're allus making trouble.'

'Oh, am I? Righto, then, I'd better make some for you.'

Joby turned round. He was fed up with Gus spoiling things.

'Look, lay off, Gus, will you?'

'I will if I want to.'

'Well want to, then. We've paid to come in so let us alone.'

'I'm not doing owt to you.'

'You're messing about with Snap.'

'What's that got to do with you?'

'A lot.'

'Oh, has it?'

'Aye, it has; so just remember.'

'Why, what will you do?'

'Just carry on and see.'

'Oh,' Gus announced to his friends, 'Joby Weston's a tough guy. I'd better be careful, else he'll bash me up.'

Joby had already turned away. He said nothing to Gus's taunting remark. He wasn't looking for a fight with anybody but he had had a few in his time. There were occasions when you just had to stick up for yourself.

But Gus didn't press the matter. He had found another amusement. Something whizzed past Joby's ear and a boy several rows away clapped his hand to his neck and looked round. Gus was shooting pellets from a rubber band looped round forefinger and thumb. You made them from cigarette cards, cigarette packets or bus tickets. You could make them from any kind of paper but the heavier it was the better they flew and the more they stung when they hit.

Joby could picture the look of innocence on Gus's face as the victim looked at the back rows, trying to spot the marksman. As soon as he looked round, Gus fired again. He was an expert with a rubber band. The boy reared to his feet, turning and shouting in fury.

'Some'dy's shooting pellets back there. Give over, will you!'

The lights faded and the boy sat down again in the darkness. Joby heard a chuckle from the row behind. That Gus! You couldn't have any peace when he was around.

The attendant, a little elderly man, was moving up and down the aisles calling for quiet in a rasping voice. Joby broke the bar of treacle toffee in two and passed half to Snap. They sucked at it as the advertisements for local shops and tradespeople flashed on to the screen. This was a boring part of the show. They saw these same advertisements week after week and nobody would really settle down until the serial began.

The attendant seemed particularly keen this afternoon to get quiet in good time. Unknown to the audience, he had had an interview with the management the day before. There had been some cases of seat-slashing during Saturday matinées and he was directed now to keep order with a firm hand and to eject without argument anyone causing trouble. He was a man who enjoyed his little temporary authority and did not mean to let a crowd of unruly kids deprive him of it and the extra cash it brought in besides his full-time job.

All this was uppermost in his mind when a pellet struck him on the cheek with the force of a hornet's sting. He flashed his torch on the back rows.

'Who's firing pellets?' he demanded. 'Come on, which of you is it?'

There was no reply as the torch beam moved along the rows.

'I can put you all out, y'know,' he said belligerently.

'Ah, go and shove your head up a drainpipe,' a voice bade him from the shadows.

The torch beam played about and fell on Joby, who at that moment was grinning broadly.

'You there. Was it you?'

Joby blinked in the light of the torch, the grin gone from his face.

'Who, me?'

'Yes, you. Come on out here.'

'I haven't done owt,' Joby said.

'Come on out here or I'll come and pull you out.'

'Oh, cripes,' Joby muttered in disgust.

Gus sniggered as Joby stood up and squeezed out to the aisle.

'I don't know what you're on about,' Joby said. 'I haven't done owt.'

'We'll see about that.' The attendant took Joby by the arm. 'Come on downstairs.'

'But I'm gunna miss the serial,' Joby protested.

'You should ha' thought about that before.'

Joby was marched downstairs into the foyer. The woman in

75

the pay-box was cashing up and there were piles of copper and silver set out in rows on the counter.

'Caught one of 'em,' the attendant said in triumph.

'I tell you I haven't done owt,' Joby said yet again.

'Let's see what you've got in your pockets,' the attendant said. 'Come on, turn 'em out.'

Joby did as he was told. It was unfortunate for him that lurking in the lining of one pocket were several pellets left over from last term when the rubber-band craze was at its height. The attendant pounced on them.

'There y'are. What's them if they're not pellets?'

'How can I shoot 'em without a rubber band?' Joby said.

'Ah, you dropped that on the floor inside,' the attendant said.

Joby fumed. He knew he couldn't win. This was grown-ups all over. Find a culprit; it didn't matter if it was the right one or not.

'I've told you it wasn't me,' Joby said. 'I've had them pellets in me pocket for weeks.'

'Are you sure it was him?' the woman in the pay-box said, looking doubtfully at Joby.

'Look, I know who it was but it wasn't me,' Joby said, appealing to her.

'Who was it, then?' she asked him.

Joby hesitated. 'I can't split, can I?'

'No, 'cos it was you,' the attendant said.

'Why don't you ask me mate, the lad I was with? He'll tell you it wasn't me.'

'Aw, he'll stick up for you, I reckon. An' anyway, I can't be messing about with you all afternoon, so you can get off home.

'You mean I can't go back in?'

'No, you can't. And you won't get in next week, neither, if I see you first. Off you go.'

'Give us me money back, then,' Joby said.

'I don't know whether you ought to have it or not, the bother you've caused.'

'You can't refuse him his money, George,' the pay-box lady said. She took four pennies off one of the piles and passed them under the glass.

'Here you are. You've made a right mess of it, haven't you?'

Joby sensed she was sorry for him. He said, 'He's got the wrong lad, but it's no use me telling him.'

'Go on, clear off,' the attendant said, 'and don't be so cheeky.'

Joby turned away towards the entrance.

'And don't let me see you here again,' the man called after him.

For a moment Joby was consumed with anger and hatred for the little man.

'I hope you get another pellet in your earhole when you get back inside,' he said.

'Be off with you, you cheeky young devil, before I clatter your face.'

The blind, daft, stupid old keff!

Joby walked sullenly away from the cinema. He smarted at what had happened. He was no angel and he had made his share of mischief; but to carry the can back for something you hadn't done. That hurt.

He didn't know what to do now, either. He couldn't go back to his auntie's before the pictures came out or she would want to know what was wrong; and she was no more likely to believe him than the cinema attendant had. So he had a couple of hours to kill while all his pals were inside watching Flash Gordon. He leant against a wall out of sight of the cinema entrance to think about it. You wouldn't expect Gus to own up to save anybody else. He was probably laughing his hat off thinking about it. Well, he'd saved fourpence and that meant he had one and three left. He could go to the model shop up George Street and buy a Dinky car—or two, if he felt like it. That was some consolation, but not enough to wipe away the sense of injustice and disappointment he felt so strongly. And it wasn't only this week. He was a marked man now. They would probably never let him in again. He was deprived of the pictures on Saturday afternoon unless he caught a bus and went down into Cressley. And that wasn't the same thing. The cinemas in Cressley were too big; he felt lost in them; and he had no mates down there. A fourpenny ticket into the flicks would cost eightpence, counting bus fares, and Snap wouldn't be able to afford that. Nor would he himself in an ordinary week when he had nothing besides his spending money. Yes, it was rotten being an outcast. Especially when you were innocent . . .

He had been standing there several minutes when Mollie Macleod came round the corner. She almost walked straight past him.

*In the second extract (which corresponds to a later scene in Part Two), Joby,
feeling wretched and having got little comfort from his preoccupied father, goes on
impulse to try to see his mother in hospital.*

'Oh, I shouldn't worry about that,' Weston said. 'It'll all come
out in the wash . . . Off you go to your Auntie Daisy's. She'll be
wondering.'

'I'll be seeing you, then.'

'Aye, so long, Joby. Be a good lad and do as your auntie tells
you.'

What did he want? Joby asked himself as he walked away from
the house. What was it he was looking for? Did he really believe
his mother was in danger, that she wasn't coming back to make
life as before? He didn't know what he did believe. Somehow the
events of the afternoon had contracted themselves into a sharp
point of loneliness and uncertainty which ripped a small tear in
the protective fabric of his world. So that now he looked through
the tear at his world and though it seemed in almost every way
the same it was in fact different. The streets, the houses, the
shops of the town where he had been born and lived all his life,
that he knew better than any streets or houses or shops any-
where—they were all the same as before, yet different because he
was looking at them through the tear. He wanted, he *needed* now,
a grown-up whom he could trust and who would, if only for a
few minutes, talk to him directly, really talk to him, person to
person, without evasions or mention of rules or fobbing him off
because he wouldn't understand. He *could* understand if only he
had the chance. But it seemed there was only one person who
would even make the attempt to talk to him like that, and she
wasn't here and he couldn't get to her.

The High Street was quieter now; people had finished their
week-end shopping and the stores were closing. He wondered if
there was still time for him to buy the Dinky cars he wanted
from the model shop. He fingered the money in his pocket as a
double-deck bus whooshed by close to the pavement. He felt the
draught of its passing round his legs and looked after it as it
stopped a little farther up the road. It was going to Cressley . . .

As he thought this the idea of the money and the bus clicked
together in Joby's mind and started him running up the pavement to leap on to the platform as the bus began to move. The
back of the driver's head seemed familiar. Joby gave him a quick

glance before running up the steps to the upper deck. If it was Uncle Ted he might have seen him on the pavement as the bus passed; but he wouldn't know he had got on.

Ten minutes later he was dropping off the bus in the middle of Cressley. He was on the edge of the market and he strolled through the lanes of empty stalls where dirty sheets of newspaper and orange-wrappings littered the cobbles—all the debris of the day's trading. A few stall-holders hung on there, selling the last of their perishable goods to women who knew the dodge of shopping late and filled bags with fruit and vegetables at a fraction of their midday prices.

The market was a forlorn place at this time of day and Joby didn't linger. On the other side he found himself on the road that led past the infirmary and he walked along it with no idea in his mind beyond the knowledge that each step took him a little nearer to his mother. There were two notices on the gate pillars: one which told you this was the infirmary and the other giving a speed limit for motor vehicles of 10 m.p.h. Beyond the trees of the drive the great walls of the hospital reared up, pierced by hundreds of windows. There were balconies too and long glass corridors joining the separate buildings. This, it struck Joby, was a place that could never stop working; a great repair shop for human beings. Sometimes people went in and were mended as good as new. Sometimes they were never properly well again. Sometimes they went in and didn't come out, because people were not like motor cars and nobody knew everything about them.

An ambulance turned the corner and came down the drive. Joby stood aside and watched it pass by and move away down the hill towards the centre of the town. A moment later he was walking up the way the ambulance had come, towards the main entrance of the hospital.

Is was ridiculously easy to get inside the hospital, because there was no one about to stop him. There must be people—the buildings were surely full of them—but he could see nobody. And nobody apparently noticed him as he crossed the courtyard and went up the steps to the doors. He looked in through the glass of the doors for a minute before pushing them open and stepping inside. The hall was a vast place with a tiled floor and long leather-covered benches. Two nurses passed through on the far side and their soft, restrained laughter echoed up in the high vaulted ceiling. Joby stood back behind a pillar, though why he was hiding from them or what he hoped to achieve here he didn't know.

When the nurses had gone he waited a minute then ventured a few steps into the open hall. There were a lot of doors about and corridors leading away into the heart of the building. On one wall, between two high narrow windows, hung an oil painting of a man with glasses and a big moustache. He wore a mayor's gold chain over the shoulders of his dark high-fronted suit. There were also some polished brass plates with lettering on them that Joby couldn't read because they were fixed too high on the walls.

He was moving towards one of the plaques to see what was written on it and was caught so, isolated in the middle of the great hall, when a swing door with a round window was pushed back and a stout grey-haired woman in a pink-and-white nursing uniform walked briskly through. He thought at first she hadn't seen him; then she changed course and came towards him, her voice echoing like those of the other nurses as she started to speak to him from twenty feet away.

'Now, young man, what do you want?'

Her eyes glinted behind her rimless glasses; with humour or irritation, Joby couldn't tell. He stammered as he began speaking and his heart was knocking uncomfortably.

'I was looking for me mother.'

'Are you with her?'

'No, I'm on me own.'

Her glance flicked over him, taking all in.

'Have you been sent here for treatment? Is there something wrong with you?'

Joby shook his head. 'No, I'm just looking for me mam.'

'Is your mother a patient here?'

'Yes, she's inside.'

'Ah, I see. Well, I'm afraid you can't see her. Visiting hours are over, and little boys aren't allowed in anyway. What's her name?'

'Mrs Weston . . . I wanted to find out how she was going on, so I came up.'

'Hasn't anybody visited her?'

'Me dad comes,' Joby said. 'He came today.'

'Well, hasn't he told you how she is?'

'He says she's all right; but I wanted to find out for myself.'

The nurse looked at him for a long moment until Joby felt himself blushing under her gaze and his heart beat faster still. She was going to tell him to go: he'd no business here, meddling into grown-up affairs. Instead she said:

'You wait here. Don't go wandering off.'

She walked away across the hall, round a corner, and out of sight. Joby waited, wondering where she had gone and what she was going to do. A stretcher came by, rolling noiselessly on rubber wheels, pushed by a man in a white tunic. There was someone on the stretcher, lying very still with blankets drawn right up to the chin. His mother must have looked like that after her operation; a white unconscious face protruding from taut blankets. His mother helpless in the hands of people whose job it was to look after her, though they didn't really care. How could they? They didn't know her. What was his mother to them except one of hundreds of patients?

He had no means of knowing how long he stood in the huge empty hall; but as he waited through the dragging minutes for the nurse to return the strangeness and impersonality of the hospital seemed a tangible weight that bore down oppressively upon him. He felt very far from home, not only in terms of exaggerated distance but in his knowledge that for the first time in his life he could not think of home as a secure embracing whole. It was incomplete. The heart had been taken out of it. It was a spick and span house in which a solitary pre-occupied man laid a table with the bare necessities for a lonely meal.

The vision frightened Joby. He wanted to run from it and from all the other images of the day that flashed through his mind: Agnes Macleod lying with the boy in the wood; the mocking, laughing face of her sister Mollie as she crouched in the tall grass; the fight with Gus, and the shame of being sent out of the cinema. He wanted to run from it all into the warm secure heart of life. His heart fluttered. He felt the trembling of his limbs and became aware that his entire body was quivering and painfully tensed, drawn out quivering and taut as though poised on the edge of flight.

So that when the hand fell on his shoulder from behind he almost screamed in terror. The man's uniform, seen in one flashing glimpse, was instantly translated into the symbol of unrelenting authority. He twisted free, lashing out with one arm, and ran for the entrance. He heard the man call out before the heavy door closed behind him but he ran on, hurtling headlong across the yard and down the drive. Only when he was clear of the hospital grounds did he stop and lean against a wall, holding his arms tightly folded across his chest as though to press out the pain from his lungs.

It was a few moments later that he began to cry. He was alone in the road but he was beyond caring who saw him weep and past the shame of weeping at all. For a while it was as though his mother were actually dead. He was drunk with grief. He staggered under it, unable to walk more than half a dozen steps at a time. In this way, taking a few paces, then stopping to hide his face in his arms against the wall, he went down the deserted road and into the town.

QUESTIONS FOR DISCUSSION AND WRITING

1.   Which of Joby's experiences is in your opinion the worst? Explain why you feel it to be so. Does it remind you of anything in your own life—an injustice, a piece of wrong-doing which really troubled you, or an anxiety about a parent perhaps?

2.   Joby's mother disapproves of Snap as his friend. Why do he and Joby get on well? Why do they drift apart? And why does Joby come to spend so much time with Gus and Tommy? Do you think he will be friends with either of them by the autumn? (You might like to write about a friendship which was important in your life in some way as you look back on it.)

3.   Which of the main adults in the play can you understand best? Why? For whom have you least sympathy? Is there anyone you really dislike?

4.   'You wouldn't understand, Joby. You're too young,' Joby's father says to him near the end of the play. Is he right? How much does Joby understand by the end of the play of what has happened in it? How important have the events of the summer holiday been in Joby's life?

5.   What feelings have Joby, his mother and his father for each other? Do you consider the play has a happy ending?

6.   Read the two extracts from the novel, *Joby*, which begin on page 72, then the two parallel scenes in the play. In each case, do you prefer the novel or the play version? Why? Look carefully at the different means Stan Barstow uses to put over the same material in the different forms of book and television play.

7.   Try writing your own television play from part of a novel you like or a short story. (Stan Barstow's story, 'One of the Virtues', in *The Human Element*—see *Reading Suggestions*—again about an eleven-year-old boy, would be excellent material.)

THE AUTHOR

Stan Barstow was born in 1928, the only child of a coal miner, in the West Riding of Yorkshire, where he still lives with his wife and two children. In dedicating the novel version of *Joby* to 'my mother and the memory of my father' he firmly says they 'are not the mother and father in this story' but, although the boy Joby is not to be identified with Stan Barstow, the author was, like Joby, eleven in the summer of 1939 as the Second World War threatened, and living in a very similar small Yorkshire town. Like Joby, too, he went to grammar school after that summer and then, like Vic in his novel *A Kind of Loving*, began his working life in the drawing room of a local engineering firm.

Like Vic he began to feel frustrated in this job, and developed his interest in writing. The success of his first novel, *A Kind of Loving*, a Book Society Choice for 1960 and subsequently made into a notable film, allowed him to take up writing full-time in 1962. Since then he has written two collections of short stories, *The Desperadoes* and *A Season with Eros* in 1961 and 1971, and five novels: *Ask Me Tomorrow, Joby, The Watchers on the Shore, A Raging Calm* and *The Right True End* in 1962, 1964, 1966, 1968 and 1976. He has written for the theatre, including an adaptation of *A Kind of Loving* which is also available in the *Student Drama Series*, for radio, many of his short stories having been first broadcast by the BBC, and has done a great deal of work for television, including the serialization of his own novel, *A Raging Calm,* and this dramatization of *Joby* for Yorkshire Television. He appeared in his own film profile, *Mind You I Live Here*, in the BBC Omnibus series.

READING SUGGESTIONS

Other books by Stan Barstow you are specially likely to enjoy are:

Joby (the novel on which this television version is based), Heinemann *New Windmill Series* or Corgi.

A Kind of Loving (the novel), Michael Joseph or Hutchinson's *Unicorn Books* or Corgi.

A Kind of Loving (the play), Blackie's *Student Drama Series*.

The Watchers on the Shore and *The Right True End* (sequels to the story of Vic and Ingrid in *A Kind of Loving*), Michael Joseph.

The Human Element (short stories taken from *The Desperadoes*), Longman Imprint Books.

A Casual Acquaintance (short stories taken from *A Season with Eros*), Longman Imprint Books.

Books by other authors which you are likely to read with pleasure if you have enjoyed *Joby* include:

One Small Boy by Bill Naughton, Longman Imprint Books.

The Red Pony by John Steinbeck, Heinemann *New Windmill Series.*

There Is a Happy Land by Keith Waterhouse, Longman Imprint Books.

Although conceived as a television play this version of *Joby*, with a certain amount of adaptation, would lend itself well to live Secondary school production. It offers a wealth of parts spanning the school's full age-range, as large or small as the varying talents and confidence of the young actors dictate. Certain simplifications would have to be made. The swift flashes from one part of a house to another, for example, so easy for television, would be impossible in live production. As an example, Joby's home could be reduced to the living-room, with one door to stairs and hall, and with Joby eavesdropping from the door rather than his bed (see *Part Four*). Some of Joby's Elsa Laedecker fantasies would probably be cut except in a very ambitious production (although the school siege could be enjoyable to stage).

The sense of place, of the child's world indoors and out, is strong in *Joby*, and in the television version over thirty scenes describe this. In a school production these could be reduced to three areas. Joby's home, the one constant area, could be to one side towards the back of the acting space (probably the floor rather than a stage). The other indoor locations, whether cinema, chapel, hospital, shop or Aunt Daisy's, could be indicated by carefully chosen properties which would lend themselves to quick and easy scene changes. The third area, between and in front of the other two, would represent, simply by the words and actions of the players, all outdoor locations such as streets, woods, or railway bridge.